Our Endangered Wildlife

ISSUES
(formerly Issues for the Nineties)

Volume 52

Editor

Craig Donnellan

Independence
Educational Publishers
Cambridge

First published by Independence
PO Box 295
Cambridge CB1 3XP
England

British Library Cataloguing in Publication Data
Our Endangered Wildlife – (Issues Series)
I. Donnellan, Craig II. Series
578.6'8

ISBN 1 86168 144 5

Printed in Great Britain
The Burlington Press
Cambridge

Typeset by
Claire Boyd

Cover
The illustration on the front cover is by
Pumpkin House.

CONTENTS

Chapter One: The Worldwide Situation

Chapter Two: The Situation in the UK

Introduction

Our Endangered Wildlife is the fifty-second volume in the **Issues** series. The aim of this series is to offer up-to-date information about important issues in our world.

Our Endangered Wildlife looks at the problems confronting our endangered species, both in the UK and around the world.

The information comes from a wide variety of sources and includes:
Government reports and statistics
Newspaper reports and features
Magazine articles and surveys
Literature from lobby groups
and charitable organisations.

It is hoped that, as you read about the many aspects of the issues explored in this book, you will critically evaluate the information presented. It is important that you decide whether you are being presented with facts or opinions. Does the writer give a biased or an unbiased report? If an opinion is being expressed, do you agree with the writer?

Our Endangered Wildlife offers a useful starting-point for those who need convenient access to information about the many issues involved. However, it is only a starting-point. At the back of the book is a list of organisations which you may want to contact for further information.

*****

Endangered animals

It is thought that there are about 10 million different species of plants and animals in the world, although only 2 million have been recorded so far. Many could soon become extinct because of the selfish activities of one species – man.

Why are so many animals in danger?

Habitat destruction

As the world's human population increases, forests and other animal habitats are cleared to make way for farming, housing, roads and industry. This is the single most important cause of species extinction.

Hunting

People kill animals for their fur (to make coats and rugs), for their bones and horn (to make medicine or ornaments), for their flesh (to eat) and just for sport. Many animals are captured in the wild for the pet trade, or for use in research laboratories, circuses and zoos.

Pollution

Rivers, seas and lakes are being polluted with sewage, oil and toxic chemicals from industry. Crops are sprayed with chemicals to kill pests which in their turn kill the animals which eat the pests.

Habitat destruction

The tropical rainforest is the world's richest natural habitat. Over two-thirds of all the plant and animal species on earth live there. Sadly it is being rapidly destroyed – half has already gone – cut down for timber and cleared to make room for farm land. If the rainforest disappears, then all the plants and animals that live there will be lost for ever.

Among those threatened is the Central African gorilla. Despite their gentle, harmless nature, these creatures have been feared and persecuted by man for centuries. Of the three sub-species, the mountain gorilla is the most endangered. There are thought to be only 700 of these amazing creatures left in Uganda, Rwanda and Zaire.

Pandas live in the bamboo forests of China which are also being destroyed to make way for a rapidly growing human population. Many years ago, pandas were found all over China; now there are just 1,000 or so, left high up in the mountains in the south-west of the country. Efforts to save the panda bear have concentrated on creating reserves and trying to protect the little bit of forest habitat that remains.

Hunting

The tiger is just one of many species of wild cats that now face extinction because of hunting and habitat loss. At the beginning of this century over 100,000 tigers roamed across much of Asia, from Turkey to India and Siberia. Today it is estimated that there are fewer than 5,000 tigers left. Already three of the eight sub-species (the Bali, Caspian and Javanese tigers) are extinct. There are thought to be only 200 Siberian tigers left and the South China tiger may already be down to single figures. In the past tigers were hunted for their skins and for sport. Today they are hunted because virtually all their body parts, including bones, eyes and whiskers, are used in oriental medicines. Many of the countries where tigers live have recently signed up to the conservation agreement known as CITES (see box) and have agreed to ban the trade in tiger products. Enforcing the laws, however, is difficult because the criminals who kill tigers and trade in their body parts make a lot of money.

Whales have been ruthlessly hunted for centuries and, as a result, several species have been driven almost to extinction. In 1982, the International Whaling Commission (IWC) voted for a moratorium (ban) on all commercial whaling starting in 1985. Norway and Japan, however, continue to kill some whales because of the loophole allowing whales to be killed for so-called 'scientific research'.

Rhinos have roamed the earth for over 40 million years but soon they could be extinct because of man's greed. The world population of all five species is now less than 10,500 animals. The number of African black rhino has crashed from 100,000 animals in 1960 to less than 2,500 and there are now only 80 Javan rhino left. Rhinos are killed for their horn which is ground up and used as an ingredient in traditional Asian medicines. This is despite a CITES ban on the trade.

The African elephant, the world's largest land animal, also faces extinction. A century ago there were 10 million; 10 years ago there were 1 million; but today there are only about 500,000 left. Elephants are killed for their ivory tusks, which are made into trivial trinkets and jewellery. In 1989 CITES banned the sale of ivory and other elephant products. This was a major conservation breakthrough and has meant that far fewer elephants are now being shot. But as the human population in Africa grows there is less room for elephants. This has meant that some African countries have started selectively killing (or culling) elephants in their game parks to keep their numbers down.

CITES

CITES (The Convention on International Trade in Endangered Species) is a United Nations agreement that protects endangered species by regulating or banning the trade in wild animals and animal products. The trouble is that not every country belongs to CITES and even many of those countries who have signed up to the treaty don't enforce it properly.

Pollution

Many of the world's wild animals are threatened by the pollution which results from man's industrial and farming activities.

It is thought that 150,000 different chemicals (including heavy metals, pesticides and industrial waste) are dumped and washed into the sea every year. The animals who live in the oceans, particularly those at the ends of the food chains, absorb these poisonous chemicals. For example, the bodies of seals, whales, dolphins and even Arctic polar bears have been found to contain high levels of PCBs, a material which could destroy the animals' ability to reproduce.

It is now thought that chemical pollution in the sea poses as great a threat to the survival of whales as the whaling fleets did in the past.

Why does it matter?

Some people say that we should conserve animals and plants because they might be useful to us in the future. Others say that in the long term, our own survival may depend on maintaining the planet's ecosystems. This means preserving other species and maintaining the planet's 'biodiversity' (or variety of life).

Animal Aid believes, quite simply, that we have a responsibility to protect animals for their own sake and especially to protect those species which our own actions and greed have endangered.

- A recent United Nations report estimated that nearly half of all birds and mammals will be extinct within 300 years.

- The above is an extract from Animal Aid's web site which can be found on www.animalaid.org.uk

© Animal Aid

Endangered animals of the world

Life began on our planet about 3,500 million years ago. The first living things were found in the sea, and over the course of millions of years, from these early life forms, a rich variety of animals has descended. Through the process we call evolution, animals have become adapted to enable them to live in all parts of the world, sometimes in the most hostile environments.

Almost 600 million years ago, the invertebrates appeared i.e. those animals without backbones – insects and other minibeasts. The earliest vertebrates, i.e. animals with backbones, were in the form of primitive fish and appeared around 500 million years ago. From these, all the other fishes descended, as well as amphibians, reptiles, birds and mammals.

The animal kingdom is enormous and we do not know for certain how many species there are in the world. Around 1.5 million species of animal have been named and described by scientists – and over a million of these are insects. It is known that there are about twice as many animals in tropical rainforests as in any other habitat, and it is here that there are likely to be countless numbers of species yet unknown to science. It has been estimated that the total number of insect species alone could be around 30 million!

It is just possible, but unlikely, that there are a few large animals remaining to be discovered, but what we can be sure of is that the most numerous large animal on Earth is *Homo sapiens* – the human! Modern man appeared about 30,000 years ago and has increasingly come to dominate the planet. The steady increase in population was speeded up by advances in civilisation such as the Industrial Revolution and better health and medical care.

The rate in increase of the human population is slowing down in parts of the Northern Hemisphere, but it continues to rise in Third World countries, despite the effect of famine, floods, disease and war.

Allowing for the death rate, over one million more humans come into the world each week!

This population explosion means that millions of people suffer from hunger and disease, and more and more wild places are taken over, causing animals and plants to suffer too.

Extinction is for ever!

As almost everyone knows, to become extinct is to be gone for ever. Even before man's arrival on Earth, species became extinct quite naturally. Natural extinction happens when a species declines in numbers gradually but steadily at the end of its evolutionary period on Earth. The length of this period depends on how well a species can adapt to changes in climate and changes in other animals and plants around it. This process of extinction can take a very long time – sometimes several million years – and the extinction of one species is immediately followed by the appearance of another in a continuous cycle.

The case of the dinosaurs is the most well-known example of natural extinction. These reptiles appeared on Earth about 200 million years ago and dominated both land and sea for almost 100 million years. It is not certain why the dinosaurs became extinct, but their disappearance was a natural one and new species of animals evolved to replace them.

The rate of extinction has speeded up unnaturally over the last 400 years, rising sharply since 1900. This increase in the rate of extinction is directly related to the increase in the human population over the same period of time. The vast number of humans has caused great damage to the planet, as wild habitats have been taken over, forcing animals and plants into smaller and smaller areas, until some of them have become extinct. We have also polluted some habitats with chemicals and refuse, making them unfit for wildlife. These causes of extinction are known as indirect destruction.

Animals may also become extinct through direct destruction. This includes the hunting and capturing of animals. Man has always hunted and killed wildlife but when

The world's most endangered animals

Mammal	ICUN Category	No. of species remaining (est.)
Black Rhinoceros	Critically Endangered	<3,000
Mediterranean Monk Seal	Critically Endangered	<1,000
Ethiopian Wolf	Critically Endangered	<1,000
Baiji or Yangtze River Dolphin	Critically Endangered	<100
Spix's Macaw	Critically Endangered	<100
Californian Condor	Critically Endangered	<100
Bali Starling (or Myna)	Critically Endangered	<100
Eskimo Curlew	Critically Endangered	<100
Northern Hairy Nosed Wombat	Critically Endangered	<100

Source: World Conservation Monitoring Centre

early humans lived more in harmony with nature, they killed animals for essential food and clothing. When firearms were invented mass destruction of species was possible. Animals have been, and still are, killed for meat, clothing, medicines, feathers, eggs, trophies, tourist souvenirs – and sometimes just for amusement. Some species are still captured in the wild for the live pet trade, even though their numbers are dwindling.

The extinction of at least 500 species of animals has been caused by man, most of them in this century. Today there are about 5,000 endangered animals and at least one species dies out every year. There are probably many more which become extinct without anyone knowing.

'Dead as a dodo'

The dodo has become a symbol of extinction. It was a turkey-sized flightless pigeon which lived on the island of Mauritius. When sailors landed on the island for the first time in the sixteenth century, they killed the helpless bird for food. The dodo's eggs and young were eaten by dogs, cats, pigs, rats and monkeys which man had introduced to the island. The dodo, unused to predators, very quickly declined in numbers – and it was extinct by 1681.

Greater horseshoe bat

There are fourteen species of bat in Britain and all of them are endangered. The greater horseshoe bat is one of the rarest. One reason for their decline is the destruction of suitable roosting sites, such as old buildings and hollow trees. They have also suffered from the use of insecticides (poisonous chemicals sprayed on to crops to kill harmful insects) which have deprived the bats of their insect food.

Siberian tiger

Cold, snowy Siberia, in the USSR, is home to the largest of all the tigers, the Siberian tiger. It is highly endangered and there may be fewer than 200 in the wild, probably all in special nature reserves. Hunting and loss of habitat have reduced their numbers.

Loggerhead turtle

This threatened reptile lives in the Mediterranean Sea, as well as the Black Sea and Atlantic Ocean. In the past its main dangers were hunting for its shell and meat. Now it has to put up with tourists disturbing the sandy beaches where it lays its eggs. In Turkey, hotels have been built right on its breeding sites. Out at sea, the turtles sometimes become entangled in fishing nets and drown.

Northern bald ibis

The Ancient Egyptians used to depict this bird in their hieroglyphic writing, but it no longer lives in Egypt. Colonies of this ibis are now found in Algeria, Morocco and Turkey. Part of the ibis' decline is due to natural causes. It nests high above the ground and its eggs are so round that some of them roll out of the nest and break. The largest colony of the northern bald ibis is in Turkey, but the use of pesticides on the marshes and grasslands where it lives is reducing the numbers.

White tailed fish eagle
Before man began polluting water habitats with pesticides, this spectacular bird of prey was much more numerous than it is today. In the Middle East, its population is now very small. The bird travels long distances in search of fish, and eating a number of poisoned fish causes the bird to lay infertile or thin-shelled eggs which are easily broken.

Lion-tailed macaque
The habitat of this small monkey is India's tropical rainforests. Many of these forests have been cleared and replaced with tea and coffee plantations. Unlike some other animals, the lion-tailed macaque has not been able to adapt to these new habitats. Poachers have also captured baby macaques, often killing their parents in the process, for illegal export to collectors.

Mandarin duck
The mandarin duck may often be seen on ponds and lakes in Britain, but its native home is across eastern Asia, in Russia, China, Korea and Japan. It may be found on water which is near forests, but the forests are being felled and the water drained, making the duck more and more endangered.

Mountain gorilla
The Virunga volcanoes region in eastern Zaire, Rwanda and Uganda is the only home of the highly endangered mountain gorilla. It depends on dense forests for survival and these are steadily being cut down to make way for crop growing and livestock grazing. The gorilla is protected by law, but despite this, some of its so-called sanctuaries have been cleared, and hunters kill them for food and trophies.

Jackass penguin
The jackass penguin is the only penguin to be found in Africa, and it was once the country's most common sea-bird. It lives off the coast of Namibia and South Africa, and the waters here have been over-fished by humans, depriving the birds of their food supply. Oil pollution also threatens them, as does the taking of their eggs for food.

Blue whale
The largest animal ever to have lived on our planet, the blue whale, lives mainly in the cold waters of the Arctic and Antarctic, where it finds enough plankton to sustain it. It migrates to tropical seas to breed. The blue whale has been a protected species since 1966, but thousands were killed up until then. During the whaling season of 1930 to 1931 alone, 30,000 blue whales were killed by Antarctic whalers. Although their numbers have increased a little, there are probably less than 6,000 alive today. It will take more than one hundred years of protection before we can be sure that it will not become extinct.

Numbat
Sometimes called the banded ant-eater, the numbat was once common in the bush and forest of north-

eastern and southern Australia. It is now only found in the most western part of eastern Australia. When man introduced predatory animals such as cats, dogs and foxes, these animals ate many numbats. Their numbers are still declining because their habitat is being cleared for farming and mining.

Komodo dragon
The Komodo dragon is the largest lizard in the world and lives on a few small Indonesian islands. It is a powerful predator and can measure as much as 3 metres in length. There are about 3,000 Komodo dragons in total, but they seem to be slowly declining. They live mainly on uninhabited islands, so are in no great danger from humans. Scientists think that natural causes are to blame. There are more males than females alive, and also the natural plant life seems to be changing and the lizards are not adapting well to their new environment.

Golden lion tamarin
This tiny monkey is one of the most endangered of all animals in South America. The few that are left, about 150, are restricted to the only remaining coastal rainforest, south-west of Rio de Janeiro, Brazil. Forest destruction is the main reason for the tamarin's decline, but it is also in danger of being captured alive and sold as a pet – a strictly illegal practice which still goes on in secret. Some captive-bred golden lion tamarins have been put back into the wild in a protected area of forest.

Spectacled bear
This bear gets its name from a yellowish mask which makes it appear to be wearing a pair of spectacles! It lives in the forest-covered mountains of several South American countries. As the forests are cleared for farming, the bear's numbers fall. Even though it is protected by law, the spectacled bear is still killed by poachers for its fur, meat and fat.

Californian condor
Today there are no Californian condors in the wild – the only living ones left are kept in zoos. During the

nineteenth century this large bird of prey lived in the mountains of many areas of North America. It started to decline last century when it was killed by gold diggers who collected its long black feathers. Disturbance of its habitat by tourists, pesticides and low-flying aircraft also contributed to its final disappearance in the wild.

Black-footed ferret

The black-footed ferret is America's rarest mammal. It is probably on the edge of extinction in the wild. This ferret hunts prairie dogs on open grassland, and as this habitat has been turned into farmland, farmers have tried to eliminate the prairie dogs by putting poison down their burrows. The black-footed ferret has also been poisoned by accident.

Hooded seal

As with all animals that live in the oceans and seas, the biggest threat to the hooded seal is hunting. It lives in the cold waters of the northern hemisphere, stretching from Canada and Greenland in the west across to Iceland and Norway in the east. The male has a strange-looking hood, or pouch, of skin above its nose which it inflates when excited. The seal population has been badly affected because both adults and young have been over-hunted, killed for their skins, meat, fat and oil.

Is it important to save animals from extinction?

Some people may ask 'why bother with conservation?' We now realise that it is important to maintain the planet's biodiversity, that it is the richness (variety) of animal and plant life, its abundance and wild habitats. From a selfish point of view, we humans never know how valuable a species of animal or plant may be for us in the future, perhaps as food, medicines or specific information.

Saving endangered animals!

People all over the world are working to help save endangered animals from extinction. There are conservation organisations which try to make people aware of the problems facing wild animals. Some of the ways in which they are being saved include habitat protection, captive breeding, setting up nature reserves and parks and using alternative products in place of products from rare animals. Governments can help by making international agreements between countries to protect animals (many countries, for example, have agreed to stop hunting the blue whale). Scientists are setting up gene banks in which they keep an animal's genetic material (the 'building blocks' of a living thing) in suspended animation. This technique may make it possible in the future to 'grow' a new animal of the same species.

You can help too!

The first step towards saving animals is to learn as much as possible about them. If we know where and how they live, and what they need to survive, then it will be easier to help them. It is also a good idea to learn from our mistakes of the past, such as destroying too much rainforest and over-hunting animals. To ensure the survival of the world's animals we must learn how to keep 'sustainable populations' alive i.e. populations with enough numbers for the animals to survive on their own. The dodo and all the others which man has made extinct became so because their populations fell below a sustainable level. It is worth keeping in mind that those animals may well become the endangered animals of tomorrow.

© Young People's Trust for the Environment (YPTENC)

Animals facing extinction

Information from Animal Aid

It's hard to imagine that at the beginning of the 20th century there were an estimated 100,000 tigers in the wild. Now there are fewer than 6,000, a decline of 95% in 100 years.

India has the largest number (about 3,230) but these, as well as tigers in other parts of Asia, Russia and China, are all under threat. The two main reasons are habitat destruction and poaching – poachers can make a lot of money by killing tigers and selling their body parts, many of which are used in Chinese medicine.

Tigers are killed for their skins, too, and many other wild cats including leopards have been hunted almost to extinction for the fur trade. Although these species are now protected, there is still a lot of illegal killing taking place.

Loss of habitat due to cattle ranching, logging, war, agriculture and land clearance to house the ever-increasing human population has affected the survival of tigers and many other different animals. Also, commercial hunters kill almost any animal they see to sell as meat.

Gorillas are another species in great danger. Only about 650 mountain gorillas remain, mostly in central Africa, and they are seriously at risk from disease, poaching and all the hazards of living in a war zone.

Many primates are captured for the pet trade or in research. Vivisection is one of the main reasons for the drop in wild chimpanzee populations. Although it is now illegal to experiment on them in Britain, other countries, including America, still use them in large numbers.

The number of elephants has also dropped dramatically. At the turn of the century there were millions of Indian elephants; now only an estimated 35,000 remain. African elephants numbered 10 million; now there are fewer than half a million. For decades they have been cruelly and ruthlessly slaughtered for their ivory tusks, captured for zoos and safari parks and have seen their habitat lost to human activity.

The plight of the rhino is just as desperate. Rhinos are killed for their horn which is ground up and used in Asian medicines. Only about 10,000 rhino remain in the world. The number of African black rhino has dropped from 100,000 in 1960 to just over 2,000.

The story is the same for pandas and orang-utans, while some species of whales are also on the verge of extinction because of the way they've been ruthlessly hunted.

Different methods are being used to try and save endangered animals. These include:

- Special programmes aimed at working with local people and educating them about the value of their animals.
- More conservation initiatives including national parks and protected habitats with rangers constantly on patrol.

- Encouraging tourists to visit countries in order to see these magnificent animals at close range.

The tourist industry brings in a lot of money, and governments and local people are beginning to recognise that it is in their financial interest to protect animals, not destroy them.

We're also losing some of our wildlife here in Britain. At one time there were very few dormice left because of loss of woodlands, but this situation is gradually improving. Unfortunately it's not such good news for water voles. It is estimated that they will have been lost from 94 per cent of their former habitats. Mink have been blamed for their decline, but it is habitat loss and pollution that are the real causes. Water voles need steep banks covered in grasses and other low growing plants to survive.

Conservationists warn that 1 in 8 species of butterflies in Britain could soon be lost for ever. Half of the 54 varieties left are in decline. It is a similar story across Europe. Intensive farming and the loss of traditional woodlands and meadows are to blame.

- The above is an extract from Animal Aid's web site which can be found on www.animalaid.org.uk

Extinction

Information from the Young People's Trust for the Environment

Extinction is a word which has an uncomfortable air of finality about it, rather like death! Whereas people are rarely unanimous in their definition of the word conservation, there can be no doubt that to practically everyone (including quite young children) extinction means to be wiped out and completely destroyed. To become extinct is to be gone for ever. In fact the process of extinction follows this simple rule: 'A species becomes extinct when its deathrate is continually greater than its birthrate.' Extinction generally occurs under one of three headings:

Natural extinction
This happens when a species declines in numbers gradually but steadily at the end of its evolutionary period on earth. The length of the period depends largely on the success of the species as a whole and its ability to adjust to changes in climate and vegetation and the appearance of predators or (in the case of predators) the disappearance of prey. It is worth remembering that a species dying a natural evolutionary death is nearly always replaced by new forms or groups.

Direct extinction
This occurs when humans destroy animals in such numbers that they become completely exterminated and cease to exist as a species. The motivations for destruction on this scale can usually be attributed to one of the following reasons: (i) profit (and often – greed), (ii) competition with animals for food, habitat or both, or (iii) the sheer enjoyment of killing. We kill animals for their meat, oil, hides, fur, feathers, shells or eggs. We trade in live animals; often at the expense of a dwindling population in the wild state. Some animals are killed because of superstitious dread; others are killed to provide souvenirs for tourists. Animals are still being killed by trophy hunters and by those who take pleasure in dispensing death (from a safe distance).

Indirect extinction
Many of the species now facing imminent extinction do so not because humans have set out to destroy them – but rather because they have stepped in the path of his 'progress'. Of all the causes of indirect extinction the most widespread and devastating must be the destruction of habitat.

Record of destruction
At the present time there are about 5,000 species of animals and more than 25,000 species of plants facing extinction. Some of these are already poised on the brink of completely disappearing and may well be beyond all hope of salvation now whatever attempts might be made to save them. With the human race multiplying at the rate of one million more people every six days; the destruction of tropical rainforests at the frightening rate of 50 acres per minute; and the probable loss of approximately 800 square miles of wild habitat each day to human needs – it is hardly

surprising that there are so many endangered species of animals and plants.

It is interesting to look at the way in which the disappearance of animal species in ever-increasing numbers is related to the steady increase in the size of the world's human population over the past three hundred years. The figures look like this:

17th century – By the middle of the century there were about 450 million humans on earth and 7 animal species became extinct.

18th century – 550 million humans on earth and 11 more species became extinct by mid-century.

19th century – By 1850 the human population had increased to 900 million and 27 species were lost.

20th / 21st century – To date there are just over 6000 million people on earth. So far this century we have lost 68 species of animals.

It is worth noting that, of the animals that became extinct during the 20th century, 64 disappeared between 1900 and 1960. Since then only four species have been lost. This may be an encouraging indication of Man's awareness of the threat to Nature in recent years and his attempts (as yet all too feeble) to repair some of the damage while there is still time to do so.

• The above information is from the Young People's Trust for the Environment. See page 41 for address details.

Pandas poised on the precipice

Unless cloning comes to the rescue, these loved bears may vanish

Giant pandas have roamed the misty mountains of China for half a million years but their once extensive habitat is today pitifully small. Fewer than 1,000 pandas live in the bamboo-rich forest fragments covering the mountains of south-west China and they could be extinct within 25 years.

Breeding programmes and artificial insemination are delaying their demise. Developments in biotechnology, however, mean that cloning is now a realistic alternative for saving these animals teetering on the edge of extinction.

For the panda, with its fussy eating habits and reluctance to reproduce, duplication could be the most pragmatic approach. Pandas have particularly poor powers of procreation, preferring to eat or sleep off the effects of bamboo over-indulgence than to engage in sexual practices. Timing is crucial as females usually produce eggs once a year and are only fertile for a few days – enough to try the patience of any zoologist trying to breed them.

They live in small isolated groups in the wild and inbreeding has undoubtedly contributed to their high infertility rate. Just 10% of males are capable of mating and only 30% of females ovulate naturally according to the China panda breeding technology committee.

By Claire Cockcroft

About 100 pandas are in zoos world-wide. They are notoriously difficult to breed in captivity and cubs often do not survive. The first success story was in Beijing zoo in 1963, despite the initial confusion in determining the sex of the animals they were attempting to mate.

Several panda cubs have been born in breeding centres in China this year, including the first set of triplets, but the long-term survival rate is low.

Pandas are also threatened by poaching and the loss of their natural habitat because of the demand for land to house and feed China's growing population. Their habitat has shrunk to half the size it was in 1984 when pandas became listed as an endangered species.

Food is another problem. Pandas have the digestive system of carnivore but are vegetarians at heart. Their highly specialised diet consists almost exclusively of two species of bamboo – they spend up to 14 hours a day munching their way through 20 to 40 pounds.

The unusual life-cycle of their major food source is another a problem. Every 30 to 100 years most bamboo plants in an area will decide to flower and then die off after

dropping their seeds. It takes around a year for new plants to grow from seed but about 20 years' growth to support a panda population.

In the past pandas would simply amble away to a new region if food became scarce. This is no longer possible as their islands of bamboo forest are separated by farmland or housing. Some pandas have starved to death.

To preserve endangered species, genes of rare plants and animals are being assembled in 'frozen zoos' in laboratories around the world. These 20th-century 'Noah's arks' contain the information from which these species may be cloned in the future. While cloning could restore the numbers of endangered species, some scientists are worried that it would produce a population lacking genetic diversity, which in itself would be a threat to survival.

The Chinese strongly believe in preserving these enigmatic bears once treasured by their emperors. The arrival of Dolly the sheep prompted the authorities to initiate a panda cloning research programme. As fertile female pandas are scarce, and panda eggs are preferentially used for artificial insemination programmes, they have pioneered the use of eggs from other species.

Earlier this year the team, led by Professor Chen Dayuan, announced the successful cloning of a panda embryo. The genetic information from the cells of a dead female panda were introduced into the eggs of a Japanese white rabbit from which the nucleus had been removed. For the gestation of this embryo, a suitable surrogate species, with similar gestation period and genetic make-up, has to be found. The success rate in obtaining a live birth from a cloned embryo is very low: 276 attempts were required to produce Dolly. And it is not known what the effects of using a surrogate egg will be on the clone.

Nevertheless, scientists hope that the first panda clone will make its debut early in the next millennium. Cloning has already been used to save other endangered species. In New Zealand, Lady, the last member of a rare breed of cow, has been cloned. Then there's the Missyplicity

project in Texas – a $2.3 million investment, largely from the owners of a dog called Missy, to clone their pet and generally understand more about cloning animals. Australian scientists are contemplating cloning the extinct Tasmanian tiger.

A woolly mammoth, preserved within the layers of Siberian permafrost for 23,000 years, might be resurrected by cloning. The nucleus of a woolly mammoth cell would be injected into an elephant egg and the cloned embryo implanted into a surrogate elephant mother, who would carry and give birth to the mammoth clone.

Although cloning has the potential to restore the numbers of endangered species, it does not solve the problem of habitat destruction. As humans have upset the balance, they have a moral responsibility to preserve species diversity. Combining bio-technological methods with a better understanding of animal reproduction and improved environmental management could help to accomplish this.

Without our intervention, endangered species face an uncertain future.

© Guardian Newspapers Limited, 2000

Hawksbill turtle faces extinction despite years of conservation efforts

By Paul Brown, Environment Correspondent

A report showing that six of the world's seven species of marine turtles are still in danger of extinction was presented to delegates of 140 countries in Nairobi yesterday. It makes a strong case for continuing the international ban on trade in turtle products.

The delegates are attending the 11th Convention on International Trade in Endangered Species, which is considering an application from Cuba and Dominica to reopen the trade in tortoiseshell. The shells are bought by Japan, where expert craftsmen turn them into jewellery.

The World Wide Fund for Nature (WWF), which is involved in many international schemes to save the turtle, says that despite some successful interventions to protect breeding grounds, all the species are still endangered including the hawksbill which Cuba particularly wants to trade. Turtles are still much in demand worldwide to be stuffed, varnished and mounted. The shells are sold openly to tourists in Vietnam, Cambodia and the Caribbean, despite the international ban.

Although tourists carrying such trophies back to Britain will have them confiscated by customs, the WWF does not believe that international policing efforts are good enough elsewhere. If the ban is lifted, it argues, smuggling and illegal killing will rise.

Elizabeth Kemf, for the WWF, said: 'Controls in the main importing country, Japan, are inadequate. The status of the turtle populations in the Caribbean is unclear. Hawksbill turtles are facing an ever-growing number of threats.'

Up to 300,000 turtles are killed each year as a 'bycatch' in trawling and shrimp nets, and on long lines used to catch tuna and swordfish. Tourism is also a threat because some of the species' favourite sandy breeding beaches have been taken up by hotels and blocked by sea walls.

The WWF believes that despite conservation efforts the future of this reptile, which has existed on the planet for 100m years, remains in doubt.

Although it is known where turtles breed, exact numbers are hard to calculate because after hatching they disappear for 10 years until they reach sexual maturity. Arguments about 'sustainable harvesting' are difficult because no one knows how large the replenishment stock is. Turtles live for 30 years, so the same adults can be recognised returning to home beaches to breed.

© Guardian Newspapers Limited, 2000

Tigers on brink of extinction

In 10 years they may all be gone

India is failing to protect its tigers, which are being driven rapidly towards extinction by poaching and habitat loss, according to a fiercely critical United Nations report to be published next week.

Unless the country takes radical action now to halt the decline, including the setting up of a high-powered national wildlife crime unit, Indian tigers will disappear within five to 10 years, UN officials believe. There may be fewer than 3,000 animals left in the country.

The senior official behind the report, Rob Hepworth, said yesterday: 'We believe the rate of decline of India's tiger population is accelerating and is now close to being in free-fall.' Some of the country's tiger reserves may no longer hold tigers, he said.

The report, to be presented next week to the Nairobi conference of the UN's Convention on International Trade in Endangered Species (Cites), is an indictment of India's attempts to look after the animal that symbolises the sub-continent's wildlife.

In uncompromising language, it lists a catalogue of weaknesses in the official tiger protection regime, on which up to $150m has been spent, much of it on tiger sanctuaries. They include lack of concern, lack

By Michael McCarthy, Environment Correspondent

of effort, lack of resources in the right place, lack of co-ordination, and corruption and a 'culture of cover-up'. The report alleges that tiger losses to poachers are deliberately concealed by government officials, and figures for the remaining animals deliberately inflated.

The report is the work of the Cites Tiger Mission, a year-long inquiry into the status of the tiger in all 14 Asian countries in which it remains, from Siberian Russia to the island of Sumatra.

The World Wide Fund for Nature estimates that less than 100 Chinese tigers remain in the wild

The mission's main concern was the continuing demand for tiger bones for use in traditional Chinese medicine – the driving force behind poaching. It aims to set up a global plan to save the animal, to be discussed at next week's conference.

The mission concluded with three 'high-level' visits earlier this year to the governments of China, Japan and India by Cites' three most senior figures: the secretary-general, Willem Wijnstekers, who is Dutch, and enforcement officer John Sellars, and the chairman of the Cites standing committee, Rob Hepworth, who are both British.

In a frank, critical report, they say that both China and Japan have made strides towards discouraging the use of tiger bones, but have had little success against poachers.

'The mission was not convinced that [Indian] tigers outside designated protected areas, or indeed those inside other than showcase reserves, are being properly protected or valued,' they report.

They call for donors to stop funding tiger conservation in India 'until central and state governments demonstrate that such monies will be spent, effectively, in total, and where they are needed'.

The programme is basically flawed, they allege. 'India's whole approach to tiger conservation and the combating of illicit trade is worthy of detailed, in-depth and independent review.'

As a matter of urgency, they say, India should set up a national wildlife crime unit to investigate and

OUR TIGER SANCTUARIES ARE FUNCTIONING PERFECTLY WELL...

WE'VE HAD NO POACHING OR CORRUPTION PROBLEMS...

... SINCE WE RAN OUT OF TIGERS...

SK

take action at state and national level. 'If this is not done, the decline will continue,' said Mr Hepworth, who, is also the senior international wildlife official in the British Government's Environment Department.

Not the least of the report's findings was that Indian tiger poachers were not being jailed. 'The manner in which arrested poachers . . . are regularly supported by experienced and well-staffed legal defence teams, out of all proportion with what such individuals might be expected to afford, provides further grounds to suggest the presence of organised criminal networks,' it says. 'Persons charged with serious wildlife crimes and repeat offenders are regularly granted bail.'

Although some officials in tiger conservation are dedicated and determined, the report says, many are not.

'Officials were clearly embarrassed when questioned closely regarding the practical implementation of the various schemes that are, outwardly, in place to further conservation and tiger protection,' it says. 'Madhya Pradesh prides itself as being India's "Tiger State" but the mission found the responsible officials to be, in the main, evasive when questioned about what work was actually taking place at field level.'

Many conservationists believe that official figures for tiger populations are inflated. The report says: 'State administrations appear to deliberately conceal the loss of tigers to poachers.'

Some forest guards do not have vehicles, weapons or radios, the report goes on. Guards in some parts of India have not been paid for 21 months. It adds: 'The mission heard, from officials at all levels, of corruption and collusion among enforcement staff.'

Mr Hepworth said Cites would expect a response from the Indian government within nine to 12 months on its demand for a national wildlife crime unit.

'There's only a very few years left for the tiger,' he said. 'Three sub-species are extinct already and there could be no tigers in five to 10 years, possibly less.'

A century ago an estimated 100,000 tigers lived in the forests and grasslands across Asia, from the Caspian Sea to Bali in Indonesia, but in the past 60 years nearly all the grassland and much of the forest has gone, and with it the tigers.

The three sub-species already extinct are the Bali, Caspian and Javan tigers. The World Wide Fund for Nature estimates that less than 100 Chinese tigers remain in the wild; they are classified as 'functionally extinct'. Around 450 Siberian and 300 Sumatran tigers are still in existence.

Between 1,100 and 1,800 Indo-Chinese tigers are thought to be scattered through Burma, Malaysia, Thailand, Laos, Cambodia and Vietnam.

The Bengal tiger, India's sub-species, also occurs in Bangladesh, Bhutan and Nepal. The population may now be as low as 5,000 animals.

© The Independent
April, 2000

A future for tigers?

The promotion of charismatic species, such as the tiger, is an important way of mobilising popular support for habitat conservation. Peter Jackson says there is still a chance to save the tiger from extinction in the wild – if there is a will to do so.

Humans and tigers have co-existed since time immemorial at the summit of food chains which form part of the complex web of life on earth. They have gone about their lives conscious of, but not dependent on, each other's existence. Today, humans dominate the world, and the tiger is at their mercy.

Throughout the ages, the tiger has had a remarkable impact on the human mind. Millions of Hindus worship the image of Durga, the powerful female deity, who rides a tiger. Siva, God of Destruction and Creation, is enthroned on a tiger skin. Tigers feature in Buddhist culture in China, Korea and Japan. And in the forests, tribal people still tend simple shrines to the tiger. For many Asians, the power of the tiger is sought in its bones to cure disease. In the western world, the tiger has inspired art and poetry, and has been adopted as the advertising symbol of leading businesses. Yet we humans are near the verge of wiping out this majestic animal.

Nobody really knows how many wild tigers there are. Counting such a secretive animal is immensely difficult, and most estimates are little more than guesses. However, there may be between 5,000 and 7,500 – a small fraction of the 100,000 which may have roamed the forests a century ago. An exploding human population, conversion of wild lands for settlement and agriculture, and ruthless hunting of its prey, and of the tiger itself as a trophy and a pest, have brought the tiger to its present plight. Three of the eight sub-species – Bali, Javan and Caspian – are already extinct, and the South China tiger is on the brink. Can the others survive the coming century?

Although there had been concern about the tiger's decline, it was only in 1972 that serious conservation efforts began. India, under the determined leadership of Prime Minister Indira Gandhi, launched Project Tiger, and the Bengal tiger began to rebound. Behind the Iron Curtain, the USSR had long before started to rehabilitate the little-known tigers of eastern Asia.

Most people associate tigers with hot countries, but in Russia, China and Korea tigers thrive in winter snows and sub-zero temperatures. They are widely known as Siberian tigers, but, in fact, their home is not the dark coniferous forests that stretch across northern Russia; they live in deciduous forests in latitudes similar in Europe to those between Rome and Berlin, and in North America between Denver and Calgary. They are best referred to as Amur tigers, from the Amur river basin which has always been their homeland.

In mid-century, their numbers in Russia had been reduced to fewer than 50, although China and Korea still had many hundreds. The Soviet government initiated strict conservation measures, and by 1990 there were about 400 Amur tigers in Russia, while those in China and Korea had been reduced to a mere handful.

The collapse of the USSR created a new crisis for the Amur tiger. As the economy fell into disarray, law and order collapsed. People in the Russian Far East, traditionally hunters, began to compete with tigers for deer and wild boar as food. The tiger itself became a target because its bones and other body parts were in demand in China for medicine, while skins could be sold for as much as $10,000 in Japan and South Korea. Poaching reached levels between 1992 and 1994 that provoked fears of the Amur tiger's early extinction. A Russian minister declared that the tiger population had been reduced to fewer than 200. International organisations rushed aid to equip anti-poaching units, which proved effective in lessening poaching, while a ban in China strengthened border controls on the illegal trade in tiger products.

Meanwhile, Russian and American scientists studying tiger ecology used the winter snows of 1995-96 to track tigers and analyse their footprints in order to estimate numbers. The results were heartening: 330-371 adults and 85-94 cubs. Clearly the Amur tiger was surviving. Importantly, nearly all these tigers constitute a single sub-population in continuous forests in the territory of Primorye and part of

Extinction of the wild tiger would provoke a deep sense of loss among many people at the elimination of a powerful symbol of the natural world

Khabarovsk. This may be the largest single population left and from a genetic point of view it is a healthy situation.

Large blocks of potential tiger habitat also exist in south-east Asia, but the dense rainforests make counting tigers and other animals exceptionally difficult. Ground surveys suggest that tigers have been greatly reduced in numbers. But there could be more than thought; camera traps in Way Kambas National Park on the Indonesian island of Sumatra have led to identification of 37 tigers where local people had scarcely seen any.

India boasts more than half the world's surviving 5,000-7,500 tigers, but the population has been heavily fragmented by loss of habitat. Only three reserves are estimated to have over 100 tigers, and some have fewer than 30.

Has the wild tiger a future? The vulnerability of isolated small groups of tigers to poaching and genetic deterioration through inbreeding, along with continued habitat loss to human use, suggests that numbers will continue to decline. The larger sub-populations have a reasonable chance. But, ultimately, the tiger will only live on if people are willing to coexist with it. The tiger is potentially a danger to livestock and even to human lives. Effective management of tigers to minimise damage to human interests, along with wise behaviour to avoid confrontation, is necessary.

Extinction of the wild tiger would provoke a deep sense of loss among many people at the elimination of a powerful symbol of the natural world. Not only would it remove a key species from the web of life on which we all depend, but it would bode ill for the survival of other threatened wildlife, perhaps even for ourselves if the natural foundations of life continue to be destroyed.

• Peter Jackson is Chairman of the Cat Specialist Group at the World Conservation Union (IUCN) in Switzerland. *Cat News*, the group newsletter, is available for a minimum donation of SF45/$40 to Friends of the Cat Group, c/o Peter Jackson, Route des Macherettes, 1172 Bougy, Switzerland.

© People & the Planet

Elephant facts

Information from Care for the Wild International

There are two species of elephant, the African elephant, *Loxodonta africana*, and the Asian elephant, *Elephas maximus*. The African elephant is larger with bigger ears, and it has two 'fingers' at the tip of its trunk, whereas the Asian elephant only has one.

There are between 300,000 and 500,000 elephants in Africa. Elephants can live in all major habitat types, from the deserts of Namibia to the tropical forests of central and west Africa. There are two sub-species, the bush elephant, *Loxodonta africana africana*, and the forest elephant, *Loxodonta africana cyclotis*. The bush elephant is far more numerous and widespread and at one time it lived throughout Africa, apart from the Sahara desert. The forest elephant is found only in the rain-forests of west and central Africa. It is smaller and has downward-pointing tusks. There are only about 40,000 Asian elephants left in the wild, and a further 15,000 in captivity. There are three sub-species of Asian elephant: *Elephas maximus indicus* is the most widely distributed, occurring in Bangladesh, Bhutan, Borneo, Cambodia, China, India, Laos, Myanmar, Nepal, Peninsular Malaysia, Thailand and Vietnam. The Sri Lankan Asian elephant, *Elephas maximus maximus*, and the *Sumatran Asian elephant, Elephas maximus sumatrensus*, are only found on the islands of Sri Lanka and Sumatra respectively.

Elephants live for about 65 years and their rate of development is similar to humans; they are dependent on their mother for about ten years and reach adolescence between 10-13 years. Unlike humans, however, elephants continue to grow throughout their lives. Elephants weigh between 900kg for a small, female forest elephant to 3,500kg for a large male bush elephant. Their height can be between 1.7m and 3.4m at the shoulder.

Elephants are highly intelligent animals and have a complex social structure, based around family groups which are led by an old and experienced female, known as a matriarch. The matriarch knows where to find water in the dry season and leads the herd's migration between dry and wet season feeding grounds. The family groups of Asian elephants and African forest elephants tend to be smaller than those of bush elephants. Related family groups maintain friendly bonds over long periods of time, and such larger associations are known as clans. Elephants communicate using various types of vocalisations, some of which are at frequencies too low for the human ear to detect.

Female elephants are able to give birth when they are in their early teens, and can have a calf every 3-4 years. The calf is born after a gestation period (pregnancy) of 23 months, and is already three feet tall and weighs 130kg at birth. A baby elephant suckles for up to 2 years. Females remain with their families all their lives. Young calves are cared for by older females and the whole group is very protective of young babies. Males stay in the family group until they are about 10 years old, when they leave and form groups with other young males. These male groups are not closely bonded, and there is much competition for rank. Only high-ranking males get to mate with females, so only the genes of the strongest males are passed on to the next generation. Older males may live a solitary lifestyle.

Tusks

Tusks are actually long teeth. An elephant uses them for many things, including lifting heavy objects and digging for water or minerals. The tusks first appear when the elephant is 2 years old, and they grow about 9-10cms each year. The largest tusks ever found belonged to an African bull (male elephant) and weighed 107kg. Female Asian elephants and some male Asian elephants do not have tusks.

Trunk

The trunk is in fact an extension of the upper lip, and is used for touch, smell, and for transferring water to the mouth during drinking. Elephants also suck up water with the trunk and then blow it over their bodies, giving themselves a shower! The trunk is very agile, and an elephant can use it to pick up both large and small objects.

Ears

The African elephant's large ears are important not only in hearing and helping to pin-point the direction of sound, but also in keeping the elephants cool. The ears are richly supplied with blood vessels, and help the elephant to lose heat from its body.

Feet

Elephants can move almost silently because a large mass of spongy tissue in their feet helps to cushion their foot falls. There are five toes inside the foot, but the number of nails can vary from four or five on the fore-feet and three to five on the hind-feet.

Elephants and ecosystems

Elephants have a major impact on their habitat. They can knock down trees, allowing grassland to regenerate and encouraging new growth in 'coppicing' type plants like Commiphora. They dig for water and minerals and these excavations can lead to the formation of water-holes. They carry away large quantities of mud on their bodies, enlarging and maintaining water-holes and ponds. They create paths which open up thickets to other species and direct run-off rain water towards water-holes. They help to disperse seeds, which pass unharmed through their digestive system.

Threats to elephants

- Poaching: Poaching for ivory reached a critical level during the 1970s and 1980s. The number of elephants in Africa plummeted from 1.3 million in 1979, to about 600,000 in 1989, when the international trade in ivory was banned. The level of poaching fell dramatically between 1989 and 1997 as a result of this ban. However, there are fears that poaching may return following a 1997 decision by CITES which allows a limited trade in ivory to begin again in 1999.
- Habitat loss and fragmentation: Elephants have dry season feeding areas, near permanent sources of water, to which they migrate when water is short. As more land is being used for agriculture and urban development, elephants are becoming confined to smaller and smaller patches of habitat. Habitat fragmentation disrupts migratory routes. Deforestation has destroyed much elephant habitat in Asia.
- Conflict with humans: The growth of the human population and the expansion of agriculture has brought elephants into increasingly close contact with humans. Elephants are often persecuted if they damage crops or property. 'Problem Animals' are sometimes shot.
- Sport hunting: Some African countries allow elephants to be hunted for sport. They argue that the revenue generated can be used for conservation. But many people think that the hunting of elephants is cruel and consider that tourism is kinder and more profitable.

Protecting elephants

Many elephant range states have National Parks or other protected areas designed to protect elephant habitat. Most elephant populations are listed on Appendix I of CITES, which prohibits international trade in them or their parts. However, it could become more difficult to enforce this ban once Botswana, Namibia and Zimbabwe, whose elephant populations are on Appendix II, begin selling ivory again in 1999.

How we help

Care for the Wild International (CFTWI) supports elephant conservation in many ways:

- CFTWI runs an adoption scheme for orphaned elephants in Kenya. The orphans are cared for by Daphne Sheldrick and her dedicated team of keepers. The orphans are gradually rehabilitated over a period of many years and join the wild elephant herds of Tsavo National Park.
- CFTWI is installing bore-holes and fire-breaks in Tsavo National Park. This will safeguard the Park for wildlife and ensure that they do not need to wander out of the safety of the park in search of water.
- CFTWI provides vehicles, equipment and mechanical expertise to assist in the work of anti-poaching patrols in Kenya and Zambia.
- CFTWI provides briefing documents and information about elephants and ivory for CITES delegates and other policy makers.
- CFTWI funded two members of the Maasai Environmental Resource Coalition to attend CITES '97.
- CFTWI has produced an informative book about elephants and their conservation.

• The above information is from Care for the Wild International. See page 41 for address details.

The Orangutan Foundation

Orangutans

Orangutan means 'Person of the forest' in Malay. Ten thousand years ago, orangutans were found throughout South-east Asia ranging all the way into southern China. Their populations probably numbered in the hundreds of thousands.

Unfortunately, the species today is found only in relict populations on the islands of Borneo and Sumatra. Orangutans are in grave danger of extinction because their sole habitat, tropical rainforest, is being destroyed by agriculture and mechanised logging. In fact, the destruction of tropical forests throughout the world with subsequent global climatic and ecological changes is one of the most pressing conservation concerns today.

Large-scale gold and diamond mining concessions pose new threats to tropical rainforests in Borneo while local population pressure is severe in Sumatra. Through illegal trafficking, countless orangutans die when their infants are captured for the zoo and pet trade. In the interior of Borneo and northern Sumatra, aboriginal people still occasionally kill orangutans for food.

Why save orangutans?

'When we try to pick out anything by itself, we find it hitched to everything else in the universe' – John Muir

'Concern for orangutans indicates concern for the plant' – Birute M.F.Galdikas

- In the past there were probably hundreds of thousands of orangutans, but no more than 15,000 survive in the wild with their number declining daily and if the current rate of habitat loss is not halted then in the wild the Orangutan is in danger of extinction within the next 10 years. Orangutans are **highly endangered**. Unfortunately, the species is found only in relict populations on the islands of Borneo and Sumatra. Orangutans are in grave danger of extinction because their sole habitat, tropical rainforest, is being destroyed by permanent agriculture, mining and mechanised logging. As great apes, orangutans are sentient beings who deserve respect of life.

- Orangutans are the largest arboreal (tree-dwelling) animals; their fruit-eating and seed-dispersing behaviour is of ecological significance, helping to shape and preserve tropical rain forest habitats.

- As orangutans disappear, it signals the disappearance of thousands of other animals and plant species in fragile tropical rainforest habitats.

- Orangutans are, with the other great apes including humans, the most intelligent beings to have evolved on land. As individuals, orangutans display unique and rich personalities. They provide models for human behaviour, in terms of physiology, cognition and evolution.

Why save tropical rainforests?

Without the tropical rainforests, orangutans and the other apes cannot survive.

The orangutan's only habitat is tropical rainforest. Over half of the world's rainforests have been destroyed in the last thirty years. The destruction continues at a disturbing rate with fifty acres destroyed each minute. If current projections hold, most tropical forests will be gone by the end of the century.

- Though essentially unexplored, tropical forests are the greatest source of biological diversity on this planet, supporting at least 60% of the world's species of plants and animals and 90% of all primate species. Unless tropical forests are saved, as many as a third of the earth's plant and animal species could vanish within our lifetimes.

- Tropical rainforests represent a storehouse of complex biochemical molecules which will be an important reservoir of medicines for the future. Even today, 40% of all prescription drugs contain active ingredients derived from wild species of plants.

- Destruction of tropical rainforest eliminates the natural hosts and habitats of viruses, bacteria and other disease-causing micro-organisms, facilitating their transfer to other vectors as hosts such as humans or domestic animals.

- Tropical rainforests help regulate global climatic and local weather conditions. Where tropical forests have been annihilated locally, droughts are more prolonged.

- Destruction of insects, birds and other tropical forest organisms can lead to failure of agricultural crops that depend on species-specific pollination.

- Destruction of tropical forests could lead to changes in mixtures of gases comprising the atmosphere, leading to, among other things, agricultural disaster.

- Tropical forests protect fragile soils and watersheds, mitigating the severity of floods.

© The Orangutan Foundation

Great apes put chimps at risk of extinction

By Cahal Milmo

The decline of the world's great ape population has dramatically accelerated and could leave major species extinct within five years, an international study disclosed yesterday.

A summit of experts from 12 countries, including Britain, has been told that chimpanzees could soon be wiped out and that gorilla and orang-utan numbers are far lower than previously estimated.

The rapid rise in hunting and the destruction of habitat in politically unstable countries in Africa and Asia was pinpointed as a key cause of the decline.

Conservation International, the American research group that has produced the new figures, said 10 per cent of the planet's 608 primate species were now in 'critical' danger. Their critical status means that the animals could disappear at any time, according to experts in the field.

Professor John Oates, a primate specialist who is based in New York, said: 'We have a crisis of such immense proportions that I don't believe most people realise how bad it is. We have to stop sitting on our hands.' One study has said that in 20 years there will be no more chimpanzees. 'Well, that is being revised to 10 years, or even five,' he said.

Field studies have found that the most endangered species, including chimpanzees, orang-utans and less well-known animals such as the tamirin, could be down to the low thousands or even hundreds. A further 10 per cent of primate species are endangered, which means that they are likely to become extinct in the next 20 years, if there is no intervention.

The most urgent threats are logging, hunting, war and the millions of impoverished refugees who rely on the same forests as the primates for their food, fuel and shelter.

Participants at the primate conference, which is being held in Illinois, United States, were told that war and hunting has put a species of pygmy chimpanzee, found only in the Republic of Congo, on the brink of extinction. The bonobo, which shares 99 per cent of its genetic material with humans and might be the closest living link to our ancestors, now has a population as low as 5,000.

Civil war and hunting have drastically reduced the bonobo's range. Bonobo meat, along with that of chimpanzees and gorillas, is known to appear on restaurant menus.

Experts agree that conventional conservation measures – such as establishing national parks – failed in the Nineties.

In Indonesia, orang-utans are disappearing at a rate of more than 1,000 a year, with fewer than 15,000 remaining. Political turmoil has encouraged rampant illegal logging in the orang-utan's native swamp forests on the islands of Borneo and Sumatra, as well as the setting alight of huge forest fires and the spread of palm oil plantations.

The orang-utan's habitat shrank by 50 per cent in the Nineties, as illegal logging quadrupled, the researchers reported.

Life under threat

Information from Greenpeace

What is biodiversity?

Life on earth has evolved, and is sustained, by a range of processes: the climate, the earth's water cycle, soil production and atmospheric conditions. An abundance of different species have emerged with these processes. No one knows exactly how many living plants and animal species exist on earth, but scientists believe there may be up to 50 million.

From genes to rainforests

The term which is used to describe this enormous range of species – everything from the smallest insect to the largest mammal or to the tallest tree in a rainforest – is 'biological diversity' – or biodiversity. Included in the concept 'biodiversity' are genes – the building blocks of life – and the ecosystems – such as rainforests or grasslands – which support life.

The relationship between species and the ecosystems they inhabit is complex: species evolve in response to the habitats in which they exist, and at the same time, ecosystems are shaped by the species which exist within them.

Extinction of species

Evolution and extinction are natural processes which have been going on since life began around 4 billion years ago. As the climate warmed at the end of the last ice age, mammoths, woolly rhinos and sabre-toothed tigers died out.

The natural rate of extinction – before humans had a major effect – is estimated to have been around one plant or animal species per hundred years. Today, the destruction of the tropical rainforests alone is estimated by some scientists to be causing the loss of one species every thirty minutes.

Biodiversity under assault

Nowadays, we are losing species before we even know what they are or can begin to understand them. Out of up to 50 million species which may exist on earth, we have names for less than 2 million. For the vast majority of these, we have little idea how they function, how they interact with other species, or of the role they play – individually or collectively – in maintaining the biosphere (the living part of the planet).

As industrialisation spreads around the world, biodiversity is under assault. Habitats – like the tropical rainforests, which cover 7% of the world's land surface, but could contain half of its living species – are being cut down, ploughed up and over-grazed. Wildlife is being hunted down. The oceans are being over-fished and their whale populations have been driven close to extinction.

Yet it is not simply a case of individual species disappearing. All species exist within working eco-systems which together maintain the earth's vital ecological processes. The air we breathe, the water we drink, the food that we eat all depend on these processes. Destroy the forests and you could, for example, destroy the climate.

What is causing the loss of biodiversity?

Habitat destruction
This is by far the worst cause: according to scientists, 80% of species decline is a result of the destruction of habitat. Almost half of the planet's forests have been chopped down in this century. The earth's coral reefs, mangroves, estuaries and wetlands are under threat from development.

Even in Britain, which had already lost most of its forests by the start of the last century, the remaining 'semi-natural' habitats: hay meadows, wetlands, heaths, peat bogs and commons have been disappearing fast, because of modern agricultural methods. Many of the plants, birds and insects which these habitats supported have disappeared with them. Species such as the barn owl, the little owl and some types of bat are on the danger list.

Hunting and over-fishing
Hunting and trading in wildlife is big business. Illegal trading is threatening many species of endangered animals and plants with extinction. For instance, despite being protected, rhinos are still hunted for their horns. In 1970, there were 72,000 rhinos in the world: today there are fewer than 11,000.

The CITES (Convention on International Trade in Endangered Species) treaty, which over 100 countries have signed, is meant to regulate the trade in endangered species and to protect species such as the giant panda, the great whales, turtles and parrots. However, CITES is widely abused in some member states, by many wildlife smugglers and by tourists who may not realise they are buying souvenirs – such as corals or ivory – made of protected species.

Marine biodiversity is also under threat from over-fishing, using modern high-tech methods. For instance, over-fishing off the coast of Newfoundland on Canada's east coast, led to the collapse of the entire cod stock in 1992. In a desperate attempt to reverse the damage the Government was forced to close the entire fishery, with the loss of 30,000 jobs.

Pollution
Four whales washed up on the coast of Belgium in 1994 contained such high levels of toxic chemicals in their bodies that they could be classified as toxic waste. Routine discharges of pollution into the seas are endangering sea mammals – whales, dolphins and seals – as well as the huge diversity of ocean life.

Less routinely, large pollution incidents, such as oil spills, kill large numbers of animals. The *Braer* spill off the coast of Shetland on 5 January 1993 killed 1,300 seabirds, 11 seals and 4 otters by the end of January alone. The *Exxon Valdez* oil spill in Alaska marred 2,000km of previously unspoilt shoreline, killing many thousands of animals including endangered sea otters and American bald eagles.

What can you do?
You can help protect biodiversity in a number of ways. Use the information in this article to avoid using or buying things that threaten biodiversity and ask questions:

- Write to the ambassadors of Japan and Norway, saying what you think about their continued whaling.
  – Embassy of Japan, 101-104 Piccadilly, London W1V 9FN
  – Embassy of Norway, 25 Belgrave Square, London, SW1X 8QD
- Reduce the amount of paper you and your family use: recycle newspapers, magazines and cardboard, avoid paper products (e.g. paper plates and cups) that can't be recycled.
- Avoid over-packaged goods like fast food.
- Let your local supermarket know how you feel about eating genetically engineered foods.

© Greenpeace

Trade in endangered species

Information from the Young People's Trust for the Environment

Man has always used wild animals and plants for their products, such as fruits and seeds for food, skins for clothing, wood for fires etc. Apart from its use for basic needs, wildlife has also been exploited for luxury items e.g. ornaments and fashion. At one time, when there were far fewer people on Earth and a lot more wildlife, such exploitation did not have any significant effect on the overall numbers of animals and plants. With over six billion people in the world today the situation is now very different. As a result of pressure from an ever-increasing human population, many species of animals and plants have been greatly reduced in numbers and they will not survive for much longer if we continue to kill them for luxury items. Modern technology and knowledge means that we can manufacture or find substitutes for products from endangered species: plastic for tortoise-shell or ivory, jojoba oil for whale oil, synthetic drugs for rhino horns and tiger bones. We can live very happily without leopard-skin coats, mahogany furniture, turtle soup or pet orang-utans.

Wildlife and the law

Over the last 30 years or so there has been a growing world-wide concern that trade in endangered species should be controlled. In 1973, representatives from 80 countries met in Washington to draw up a formula for trade controls and licences. As a result of this meeting the Convention on International Trade in Endangered Species (CITES) was formed. The purpose of CITES is to decide which species in trade are in danger of becoming extinct and to establish laws to stop them from being pushed any closer by international trade. There are now at least 126 member countries and their representatives meet every two years for discussions and to decide whether any changes are needed. Environmental organisations can attend the conferences to contribute to the debates and to lobby the delegates.

When a country joins CITES, its government must pass laws to control or prohibit trade in live or dead specimens and parts or derivatives of them. The amount of trade allowed depends on which 'Appendix' (group) the species has been listed in. The rules for deciding which species should be listed in which appendix were set down at the very first CITES conference in Berne, Switzerland, in 1976, although they have been revised since then. Any member country can put forward a species for listing, or changing to another appendix, but to be adopted, two-thirds of the delegates must vote for the proposal. A proposal is usually a scientific report summarising the best available information on the status of the species and the impact of trade on it. The Convention cannot control trade between two countries who are not CITES members, but fortunately the number of member countries is slowly increasing year by year.

There are three appendices:

Appendix I – trade is totally banned for primarily commercial purposes.

Appendix II – potentially threatened species for which trade is allowed if there is 'no detriment' to the species: quotas (the numbers of individuals traded) may be imposed.

Appendix III – species requiring additional protection in their country of origin.

Enforcing the law

This is a difficult problem, especially when officials responsible for the enforcement don't take it seriously – and this happens all too often. Even CITES does not have a Law Enforcement Working Group. It is expensive to enforce a law and yet a law is useless unless it can be enforced.

Smuggling, i.e. illegal trading, is not easy to control. It is easier to

stop the poverty-stricken poacher than the rich, influential business-man, or, worse still, corrupted government official. It is also difficult for the customs officer to identify the protected species in a big shipment of animals and plants – especially as they are often hidden or disguised.

Of all the hundreds of species of animals and plants involved in international trading laws, amongst some of the best-known examples are: big cats, whales, elephants, rhinos, bears, parrots, apes and rainforest plants. Here are some brief case histories . . .

Tigers

Fifty years ago there were eight sub-species of tiger, but three are now extinct. Today, all five remaining sub-species are endangered. The total number left in the world could be as low as 5,000. All tigers are in demand by Eastern countries because of their belief that tiger bones, claws, teeth and most other body parts have medicinal properties. China, South Korea and Taiwan are the main consumers but tiger products are also exported to Chinese communities in the rest of the world. China's own tigers are almost extinct so traders have turned to tigers in other countries and much illegal smuggling goes on. Tiger numbers are also declining because of the loss of their forest habitat and a shortage of prey.

Trade laws

Most tiger countries have laws protecting them, but they are often poorly enforced. Tigers are on Appendix I of CITES but five of the fourteen countries (which include China, India, Thailand, South Korea, Vietnam, Russia and Japan) have yet to join CITES – Bhutan, Burma (Myanmar), Cambodia, Laos and North Korea. However, these five, together with the CITES members, have voluntarily pledged to stop international trade in tiger products and, within their countries, to ban the use of tiger bone in traditional medicine. These countries have formed the Global Tiger Forum to discuss ways of working together to help tiger populations recover.

The future

The protection laws must be enforced somehow if the tiger is to survive. The US government's action of imposing trade sanctions on Taiwan, and threatening to do the same to China, may help. Hopefully, the Global Tiger Forum's discussions will bring about effective enforcement. Conservation organisations have set up projects to try and control poaching and to win the support of people who live in tiger areas, and to persuade people to use alternatives to traditional tiger-based medicines.

Bears

The world's bears, like tigers and rhinos, have suffered because of a medicinal demand for their parts in the Far East – China, Japan, Korea, Singapore, Taiwan and Thailand. The bear's gall bladder is in the most demand, believed by the Chinese to be good for all sorts of ailments, from liver disease to blindness. Gall bladders are on sale throughout Asia and the trade is thriving because of increasing affluence in the Far East. China and Korea have 'bear farms' where bears are kept in cruel conditions and 'milked' for their bile (the liquid from the gall bladder).

The Asian bear species, i.e. Asiatic black bear, sun bear, sloth bear and the brown bear in Russia, are under the greatest threat. For example, Russia's Kamchatka Peninsula had about 11,000 brown bears in 1991, but only 4,000 by 1993.

The American black bear, brown bears in Europe and North America, and spectacled bears in South America, are now being poached.

Many bear cubs have been captured alive, by killing their mothers, and used as 'dancing' bears in India, Pakistan and Turkey. There has been much public opposition to these cruel practices and they are beginning to be outlawed.

Trade laws

All bear populations are listed on either Appendix I or II. They are protected on paper in many countries and in others they may be legally hunted for 'sport', but throughout most Asian countries law enforcement is practically non-existent and prosecutions are rare.

The future

Organisations such as the World Society for the Protection of Animals are campaigning against abuses of bears and public protest is causing Far Eastern governments to make greater efforts to enforce laws which are designed to protect bears. As with tigers and rhinos, it is important to promote alternative medicines to users of Chinese cures.

Leopard

Today, very few people in the US and Britain would consider wearing leopard-skin coats but in some parts of the world people still consider a leopard-skin coat to be a status symbol. Such coats may be bought by tourists in a place such as Kathmandu, Nepal, even though the traders are aware that they are likely to be confiscated by customs at the airport.

Some men regard shooting a leopard, and taking home parts of it as 'trophies', as a very macho thing to do. This 'trophy hunting' has been allowed by CITES in African countries which report leopard numbers to be adequate. These so-called 'sport' hunters are mainly from North America and Europe.

The latest threat to leopards is an increasing demand for their bones, as a tiger-bone substitute for oriental medicines. Bones are smuggled mainly into China and Taiwan from neighbouring countries.

The leopard is most common in India and Africa, though not nearly so numerous as it once was. Other races, existing in former Soviet Union, China and the Middle East, are either extremely rare or thought to be extinct. The Snow leopard, from the Himalayas, Tibet, Central Asian Republics and Mongolia, is also rare – 5,000 left. The Clouded leopard is found in forests of Nepal to South China down to Sumatra,

Borneo and Taiwan, but, although many skins turn up in China, no estimates of their numbers exist.

Trade laws

All leopard species are listed on Appendix I of CITES. Officially, they are protected everywhere although African countries allow licensed and controlled hunting for trophies. Enforcing the protection laws is difficult, especially where there is conflict with the public in areas where leopards are accused of killing children and cattle. In India, unlike tigers, leopards are not confined to reserves, where they would be well protected, so enforcing the law is more difficult.

The future

The organisation People for the Ethical Treatment of Animals is trying to discourage people around the world from buying furs, and Respect for Animals campaigns against trapping for fur. Other conservation groups investigate the fur trade and promote research and leopard conservation projects. If people no longer wanted to wear leopard-skin coats or display 'trophies', then there would be no point in continuing the trade in skins and other parts.

Parrots

Parrots have been popular as pets for years but the capture of large numbers of wild birds for mass exports to pet shops all over the world is causing a serious decline in many wild populations. The trade still thrives despite the cruelty and high death-rate involved in their capture and transit. Even common species, such as the African Grey, are beginning to be affected. A specialist collector will pay thousands of pounds for one rare bird. Although many species are bred in captivity, these are often more expensive to buy than wild-caught birds, and this encourages the wild trade to continue.

Trade laws

There are 328 species of parrot and all but three of these are listed on either Appendix I or II of CITES. In the USA, the 1992 Wild Bird Conservation Act insists that the traders prove their trade will not result in a decline in the wild population of the species. This action has resulted in a dramatic fall in the US bird trade since 1992. Bird imports into the UK have fallen by about 30 per cent each year since 1992, but there is an urgent need for similar legislation to that of the US and an effective wildlife enforcement unit.

The future

Through lobbying by conservation organisations and the public, over 100 airlines now refuse to carry wild-caught birds. Hopefully, all airlines will eventually support this campaign. If people wish to buy a parrot, they should first make sure that it has been bred in captivity.

An additional threat to parrots is the destruction of their forest habitat, and if the pet trade continues then many species are doomed to extinction in the wild in the very near future.

Plants

Although they are extremely important, and often beautiful, living organisms, plants are often overlooked when considering endangered species – animals usually attract more media attention. However, many thousands of species of plants need our help to prevent them from becoming extinct. Many commercial plants are grown in plantations or nurseries, but a large amount are still taken from the wild. Examples are the tropical hardwood trees, orchids, snowdrop bulbs, cacti and carnivorous plants, such as Venus flytraps. All these plants are removed from the wild either by the timber trade or for use as house and garden plants.

Trade laws

There are about 200 plant species listed on Appendix I by CITES. There are thousands more, including all orchids and cacti, on Appendix II. However, enforcement of the law is poor in most countries and many customs officers are not able to identify species in a shipment. Up to date, CITES has managed to list the Caribbean and Central American mahoganies on Appendix II, but fierce opposition by Brazil, Peru and Bolivia has prevented the Brazilian mahogany from also being listed – these countries have 90 per cent of these remaining mahogany trees. Japan is the biggest consumer of timber and living plants are sold mainly in North America, Europe and Japan.

The future

Various conservation organisations are either investigating the trade in plants or funding field projects. The charity Plantlife has been set up specifically to save plants.

We can all help by refusing to buy items made from mahogany, or plants taken from the wild – check their source before buying.

© Young People's Trust for the Environment (YPTENC)

The battle to save the world's rare wildlife

By Michael McCarthy,
Environment Correspondent

Two weeks of heated international debate about the hunting of rare wildlife open this morning when ministers and officials from 150 countries meet at the Nairobi conference of the Convention on International Trade in Endangered Species (Cites).

The argument will be between nations that want to preserve wild creatures and plants, and those that want to hunt them, export them, and generally use them for profit.

At the top of the agenda are the great beasts which conservationists sometimes call, with a hint of irony, the charismatic megafauna: elephants, whales, sharks and tigers. All can be turned into valuable commercial products for which there is a demand – ivory, whale meat and blubber, shark's fin and tiger bones, prized in traditional Chinese medicine – and all will be the subject of fierce arguments about their protection and use.

Four southern African countries, Zimbabwe, Botswana, Namibia and South Africa, want to reopen the trade in elephant ivory, banned around the world by Cites in 1990 when African elephants seemed unstoppably headed for extinction. Two traditional whaling nations, Norway and Japan, want to reopen the trade in whale meat which was outlawed with the whaling moratorium of 1986 when several of the larger whale species had been virtually wiped out.

Three conservation-minded countries, Britain, the US and Australia, want to move to protect the three greatest of the sharks – the whale shark, the basking shark and the great white shark – increasingly hunted for their fins or for their teeth as trophies.

And one nation, India, will come under fierce attack for its alleged failure to protect its most magnificent animal, the Bengal tiger, in spite of a protection programme that stretches across the land.

Britain will be opposing the whale and ivory moves, and supporting the drive to make India put its tiger-conservation house in order by setting up a national wildlife crime unit to combat poachers.

Further down the agenda will be arguments about a raft of humbler but still fascinating creatures, from the hawksbill turtle and the Malagasy poison frog to the ornamental tarantula of India and Sri Lanka, all of which are threatened in one way

---

Convention on International Trade in Endangered Species of Wild Fauna and Flora

What is CITES?

The international wildlife trade, worth billions of dollars annually, has caused massive declines in the numbers of many species of animals and plants. The scale of over-exploitation for trade aroused such concern for the survival of species that an international treaty was drawn up in 1973 to protect wildlife against such over-exploitation and to prevent international trade from threatening species with extinction.

Known as CITES, the Convention on International Trade in Endangered Species of Wild Fauna and Flora entered into force on 1 July 1975 and now has a membership of 150 countries. These countries act by banning commercial international trade in an agreed list of endangered species and by regulating and monitoring trade in others that might become endangered.

CITES' aims are major components of Caring for the Earth, a Strategy for Sustainable Living, launched in 1991 by UNEP – the United Nations Environment Programme, IUCN – The World Conservation Union and WWF – the World Wide Fund for Nature.

Why is CITES needed?

There are over 13,000 known species of mammals and birds, as well as thousands of reptiles, amphibians and fish, millions of invertebrates and some 250,000 flowering plants. Extinction is a natural feature of the evolution of life on Earth. But in recent times humans have been responsible for the loss of most of the animals and plants that have disappeared.

Many species are declining in number because of loss of habitat and increased exploitation as human populations grow. Trade has now also become a major factor in the decline as improvement in transport facilities has made it possible to ship live animals and plants and their products anywhere in the world.

The wildlife trade is a highly lucrative business and involves a wide variety of species, both as live specimens and as products. Millions of animals and plants are traded each year to supply the demand for pets and ornamental plants.

Fur, skins, leather and timber, and articles manufactured from these materials are all traded in large quantities.

© Convention on International Trade in Endangered Species of Wild Fauna and Flora (CITES)

or another. Cuba wants to trade annually in the endangered hawks-bill's shells (Britain is opposing this), and the frog and the spider are at risk from overcollecting for the pet trade.

Horse-trading will be the order of the day. It became clear in the Norwegian press last week that pro-whaling and the pro-ivory groups will form an *ad hoc* alliance: the Oslo paper *Dagbladet* reported last Tuesday that Norway will support the proposal to reopen the ivory trade in return for backing from the four African countries over whaling.

> *The argument is between nations that want to preserve wild creatures and plants, and those that want to hunt them*

Green pressure groups have been alarmed that in both cases decisions could be taken which would fatally undermine the whaling and ivory trade bans, although a two-thirds majority of countries voting is necessary.

Britain's Fisheries Minister, Elliot Morley, who has responsibility for whaling, will be travelling to Nairobi in person next week to lobby other Cites member states on the whaling issue. Mr Morley said last week that Britain was 'implacably opposed' to resuming the trade in whale meat.

IFAW campaigns to protect endangered species

By Sarah Tyack

International trade in wildlife is a lucrative business worth billions of dollars. The scale of this trade poses a huge threat to the survival of many species that the International Fund for Animal Welfare (IFAW) is campaigning to protect.

In 1973 an international treaty was drawn up to protect wildlife against over-exploitation for trade and to prevent international trade from threatening species with extinction. Known as CITES, the Convention on International Trade in Endangered Species of Wild Fauna and Flora entered into force on 1 July 1975 and now has a membership of 150 countries. These countries meet every two years to vote on whether to ban commercial inter-national trade in critically en-dangered species, or to regulate or monitor trade in others that might become endangered.

In April 2000 CITES met in Nairobi, Kenya. In the preceding weeks and months IFAW worked tirelessly to lobby CITES authorities of numerous countries, raising key issues in the EU and UK parliaments and raising public awareness of the significance of the decisions. We have posted the results of the CITES meeting on our web site.

How does CITES work?

Species are placed on three Appendices which form the basis of the Convention. Trade is banned in species listed on Appendix I, controlled in species on Appendix II and monitored in species on Appendix III. Any member can propose an amendment to the Appendices which can result in a species being 'downlisted' or 'up-listed'. The amendment requires consensus or, if voted upon, a two-thirds majority of those present to be passed. The Conference also adopts Resolutions, which are 'recom-mendations for improving the effectiveness of the present Con-vention'. Many of these Resolutions are also key to issues that concern groups such as IFAW.

IFAW urged the Parties to oppose the following proposals:

1. Norway and Japan had proposed to re-open international trade in whale meat, banned by CITES since 1986. Japan proposed to downlist the Minke Whale from Appendix I to Appendix II.

It also wanted to carry out the commercial hunting on Eastern Pacific grey whales. IFAW argued that these proposals were not in accordance with CITES recom-mendations on commercial whaling

and no effective management system was in place. The proposals were defeated.

2. Cuba proposed to re-open international trade in Hawksbill turtle shells. Hawksbill turtles are listed as critically endangered on the IUCN (World Conservation Union) Red List of Threatened Animals and sea turtles are already the most widespread illegally traded animal species. IFAW was very concerned that if Cuba was able to sell its stockpile of Hawksbill shells it would encourage further illegal trade and have a serious impact on the whole Caribbean population of these rare turtles. We lobbied hard to stop this threat to the turtles and the proposal was defeated.

3. South Africa proposed to re-open international trade in ivory so it could sell off its stockpile of ivory to Japan. But after the ivory trade was partially re-opened in 1997, poaching continued and concerns remained about the absence of an effective monitoring and trade control system. Again IFAW lobbied hard to stop a resumption of trade and the proposals were withdrawn. CITES also agreed to revise the existing system.

IFAW urged Parties to support the following proposals:

1. The UK proposed protection for basking sharks by listing them on Appendix II and regulating international trade in their products. Little is known about the impact of the shark fin trade on this massive fish which lives in temperate waters throughout the world. Yet there is massive demand for its fins in East Asia. Sadly the measure was defeated by a tiny number of votes.

2. Kenya and India proposed to return the African elephant population to Appendix I, thus banning any future international trade. However, following intense discussions between elephant range states, this proposal was withdrawn along with proposals to re-open the trade.

How is CITES relevant to you?

You can help CITES enforce its regulations. When abroad avoid buying anything that has come from an animal or is made of coral. If you see anything suspicious, i.e. a turtle shell, please contact the CITES Secretariat in Switzerland with details, on (+ 41 22) 917 8139/40 or e-mail at cites@unep.ch

• The above is an extract from *Animal Update*, the magazine of the International Fund for Animal Welfare (IFAW). See page 41 for address details.

Traders say profit can be motive for preservation

Today the world debates a crucial question: do you best conserve rare species by allowing some to be killed?

A battle between African states for the future of the elephant begins in Nairobi today. On one side are the countries of the south with increasing elephant herds, which want to trade ivory, hides, meat and trophies; on the other those of the north and west, which rely mainly on the tourist trade.

The latter are afraid that the resumption of trading would restore black-market prices for ivory and encourage poachers to destroy their herds and their livelihoods.

But the argument in Nairobi is not just about elephants. For the next two weeks the 150 countries which have signed the Convention on International Trade in Endangered Species (Cites) meet for the first time in three years to decide which animals, birds and plants to protect, and how to do it.

By Paul Brown, Environment Correspondent

And it is not a simple matter of deciding whether to ban trading in species that are disappearing. Rather, the argument is whether the future of many of the world's favourite

animals and plants can be better protected by controlled trading.

Twenty years ago there was still a substantial body of opinion that large areas could be fenced off, either literally or legally on paper, where tigers could romp and nature could continue unmolested.

In practical terms this often meant not consulting the people who lived in these places, and evicting them from their homes and traditional way of life, without considering that these tribes and animals may have coexisted for centuries.

Elephant and tiger were both given fenced-off areas in their home ranges, but both species need a lot of space to forage and hunt, and their needs compete with those of ever-increasing human populations which want to plant crops where these animals once freely roamed.

Conservationists and some African states will argue in Nairobi that unless local people are given an interest in keeping the elephants alive by being allowed to profit from their ivory and eat their meat, then the elephant will come off second best.

There is a slightly different approach to whales. The Norwegians argue that the minke is in direct competition with man for fish species which are in short supply, and that they should be culled as a food resource to keep their numbers limited.

The same argument applies to Hawksbill turtles. Trade in their shells is banned, but Cuba, which has a well-managed population and a tradition of eating turtle meat, much of it now farmed, has a stockpile of shells which it wants to sell to Japanese craftsmen.

The argument is that if fishing villages can profit from the sale of shells they will have an interest in protecting wild turtle stocks.

Opponents ask how, if trading is allowed, it is possible to tell whether the shell came from a farmed or wild turtle, whether the ivory came from a licensed country or was poached in another state.

Those in favour of total bans say that halting official ivory sales brought a dramatic drop in poaching. In the 1990s black-market prices collapsed and many poachers turned to other ways of making a living.

The argument is whether the future of many of the world's favourite animals and plants can be better protected by controlled trading

---

Cites lists fully protected species in which all international trade is banned in appendix I. Those in which a limited, highly regulated trade is allowed are in appendix II. The southern African states want their elephants listed in appendix II; Kenya wants them in I.

A similar battle surrounds whales. Norway and Japan believe that minke in the North Atlantic, Antarctic and parts of the Pacific, currently in appendix I, are now sufficiently numerous to be hunted and eaten under strict quota rules.

They want the minke 'down-listed' to appendix II. Conservationist countries, including Britain and the US, are appalled.

Another international body, the International Whaling Commission, controls whale hunting but it is a much smaller organisation, with fewer than 50 member states, and it is in the hands of conservationists, who have blocked the resumption of whaling.

Japan and Norway have been accused of using aid money and other political levers, like support for the ivory trade, to get Cites to take over the role of controlling whaling. They deny it.

A problem with whales, turtles, elephants, and the basking shark (which Britain wants to protect) is that they do not respect national boundaries. The basking sharks from which Norway cuts the fins to send to Japan for soup are the very fish that attract Japanese tourists to the Isle of Man, where they can be seen sailing past in the clear water.

© *Guardian Newspapers Limited, 2000*

Threatened species in traditional medicines

Substitutes for endangered and threatened species in traditional medicines

Why explore the issue of substitutes?

Many traditional medicine disciplines utilise wild plants and animals. For example, traditional Chinese medicine (TCM), the most widely practised traditional medicine system in the world, utilises more than 1000 plant and animal species. TCM is used throughout Asia and by Asian communities worldwide. In addition, it is increasingly attracting non-Asian consumers.

While TCM has been practised for perhaps 5000 years, some of the wild plants and animals long utilised are now threatened or in danger of extinction. Among these are certain orchids, musk deer, rhinoceroses, tigers, and some species of bears.

The changing status of the tiger is one of the most dramatic examples. There may be as few as 5000 tigers remaining in the wild compared to the 100,000 that existed earlier this century, and three species have become extinct in the past 40 years. Habitat loss and fragmentation played a significant role in the tiger's decline. Today, however, poaching to meet demand for tiger bone in traditional East Asian medicine is the most urgent risk to the tiger's long-term survival.

Owing to the strong allegiance to TCM as a legitimate health care system as well as its cultural significance, protective laws and trade bans are not enough to stop the use of highly endangered species in medicines. In the case of tiger-based medicines, China and other consuming countries and territories have introduced trade bans, and China has even removed tiger bone from the official TCM pharmacopoeia. However, as tiger bone has been a respected ingredient in TCM for treating painful diseases of muscles and bones for centuries, there remains a stubborn residual demand

and, therefore, a black market trade that spans the globe to meet it.

The recognition of the importance of substitutes is gaining ground among the traditional medicine industry itself and among governments. Representatives of the traditional medicine communities in Asia have expressed interest in further research and development of substitutes for highly endangered species used in TCM. In June 1997, the member countries of CITES, the Convention on International Trade in Endangered Species of Wild Fauna and Flora, adopted two far-reaching resolutions that included calls for investigation and promotion of viable substitutes that would not lead to other species becoming threatened.

Are substitutes the solution?

Substitutes are *part of* the solution. Substitutes would have to be carefully assessed to ensure they would not endanger other species. In addition, the development of substitutes alone would not save the tiger and other highly endangered species from habitat destruction and other pressures. Most importantly, substitutes would need to be accepted

by traditional medicine users as a viable alternative. Identifying a viable substitute would be only one very important step in the multi-

faceted approach necessary to conserve the tiger and other threatened medicinal species.

© TRAFFIC

Medicinal wildlife trade

Information from TRAFFIC

Goal: TRAFFIC aims to support the conservation of wild plants and animals used for medicinal purposes through the collection and analysis of biological and trade data and the development and dissemination of information and advice on medicinal wildlife trade.

Why is the medicinal trade in wildlife a priority for TRAFFIC?
- The World Health Organisation estimates that as many as 80 per cent of the world's more than four billion humans rely primarily on animal and plant-based medicines.
- Derivatives of wild plants and animals are not only widely used in traditional medicines, but are also increasingly valued as raw materials in the preparation of modern medicines and herbal preparations.
- Increased demand and increasing human populations are leading to increased and often unsustainable rates of exploitation, with some wild species already threatened with extinction as a result.
- Although a great deal of information on the use of wildlife for medicinal purposes is available from published pharmacopoeias and ethnobiological studies, in most cases little is known regarding harvest and trade volumes, trade controls, market dynamics and conservation impact.
- TRAFFIC is already recognised as a leader in investigating certain aspects of the medicinal trade in wild species, for example with regard to some ingredients of traditional Chinese medicine.

© TRAFFIC

The trouble with tourists

Information from the World Society for the Protection of Animals (WSPA)

Marine turtles thrived in our oceans during the time of the dinosaurs, more than 100 million years ago. Today, these ancient creatures are facing an uphill battle for survival. The combined onslaught of commercial hunting, egg theft, modern fishing techniques and the increasing development of tropical coastlines is threatening to make turtles as extinct as the dinosaurs.

Critically endangered

There are seven species of marine turtles: four are classified as endangered and two are critically endangered – these listings have been given because their populations have declined by anything from 50 per cent to more than 80

per cent in the last fifty years. International trade in turtles and turtle products is officially banned under the UN convention on endangered species – CITES.

For much of their lives turtles migrate huge distances but during

---

Throughout the world, coastlines which once consisted of scattered settlements and quiet beaches are rapidly being turned into endless strips of urban development

---

certain times of the year they congregate in shallow coastal waters to breed. At this time females venture ashore on several occasions in order to lay clutches of up to 150 eggs. Around two months later tiny hatchlings emerge from the sand and make their way out to sea. For many, the epic struggle of a fully grown turtle crawling on to a beach to excavate her nest and the subsequent emergence of hundreds of hatchlings is one of the wonders of nature. But this unique life-cycle has put the turtle into direct conflict with the planet's biggest industry, tourism. The tropical and sub-tropical beaches which turtles have used for millions of years have become the object of desire of a never-ending tide of tourists.

Throughout the world, coastlines which once consisted of scattered settlements and quiet beaches are rapidly being turned into endless strips of urban development. Disturbance from hotels, shops, restaurants and roadways can place an unbearable burden on nesting turtles and their hatchlings. Many females will not lay their eggs if noise or lighting from resorts is too great; nests can be damaged or destroyed by sunbathers; and newly hatched turtles can be disoriented by beach-front development and may never reach the sea.

In the Mediterranean the nesting period of the logger head and green turtle coincides almost exactly with the peak tourist season from May to August. Although protection measures have been introduced at some beaches it is thought their population has crashed from tens of thousands to only a few thousand since the 1950s.

Trouble spot

At Grande Anse, on the Caribbean island of Saint Lucia, bulldozers have moved on to the mile-long beach to start a major new construction programme. The site, which is a major rookery for leather-back turtles, had previously been earmarked as a potential National Park. Now local conservationists, who have been monitoring turtles there for ten years, are being restricted from the beach.

If turtles are to survive the continued expansion of tourism along tropical and sub-tropical coastlines, this multi-billion-dollar industry must accommodate the needs of the species.

Getting the measure of extinction

Trying to measure just how fast species are becoming extinct is a tricky business, writes Georgina Mace

For a start, we have a very in-complete knowledge of the earth's biota. Estimates for the total number of species range from 5 million to 60 million, though most experts would place the total at about 10 million. Of these, fewer than 2 million have been described.

Among animals we know the mammals and birds best. There are about 14,000 species and we know most of them. But these numbers are swamped by the one million des-cribed insects – which probably make up fewer than 5 per cent of the total.

There are around a quarter of a million described plant species, making up about half the total – and 80,000 described fungi, or about 5 per cent of the total. The remaining species – bacteria, viruses and protists – are so poorly known that nobody can credibly estimate their number. So most of what can be said about extinction relates best to larger plants, mammals and birds.

Like all species, these have been subject to extinction as a funda-mental part of evolution. Indeed, of all the species that have ever lived during the 600 million years of the fossil record, only about 2 to 4 per cent survive today.

But how do extinction rates compare with those in the past? Looking at the fossil record it appears that invertebrate species have had an average life span of 5 to 10 million years. The poorer data for mammals suggests a lifetime of perhaps 1 to 2 million years.

Of recent extinctions the best, but still very incomplete, record is for birds and mammals lost over the last century. This indicates that one species out of 14,000 becomes extinct every year – giving an average species lifetime of 10,000 years. This may sound a long time, but is 100 to 1,000 times shorter than the lifetime of species in the fossil record.

Estimating the lifetimes of extant species involves projections based on loss of wild habitat and the extinction processes of well-known species.

One species out of 14,000 becomes extinct every year – giving an average species lifetime of 10,000 years

---

Drawing on the IUCN Red List of threatened animals, published in 1996, species lifetimes for well-studied groups of birds, mammals and reptiles are estimated at approxi-mately 300-500 years. Across broader groups lifetimes are between 100 and 1,000 years. These values are similar to the estimates made using habitat projections.

So our estimates show that species extinction rates are 1,000 to 10,000 times higher than in the past. This makes current rates of species loss at least equivalent to the mass extinctions of the past – and in as short a time.

We do seem to be on the brink of a large-scale extinction spasm. But a major difference now is that almost all extinctions are due to the impact of human activities. People now so dominate the earth that very few species are completed unaffected by our existence.

• Georgina Mace is a research fellow at the Institute of Zoology (London) and a member of the steering committee of IUCN's Species Survival Commission.

Extinct – so what?

Information from the RSPB

Dinosaurs are good at being extinct. In fact, they're famous for it. It keeps them at a safe distance, and boosts their media ratings.

But what of creatures still alive, that . . .
- Don't have enough charisma to get on TV?
- Maybe haven't even been discovered yet?

Does their extinction matter?

Wildlife in our lives
Many of us see wildlife 'second-hand' through TV and films. It is not part of everyone's lives. For indigenous peoples relying on the land in developing countries, wildlife is 'first-hand'. It is at the centre of their cultures, celebrated in art, dance, song and story.

They know its importance. They use wild plants and animals for food (especially when crops fail), shelter, medicines, firewood and household utensils.

Media exposure makes household names out of 'obscure' species.
- Which of us knew much about meerkats before their 'debut' on TV?
- Would we have cared then if they had been declared extinct?
- Would we care now?

Knowing wildlife makes it 'real'. We see it as part of the diversity of life (biodiversity). We are more likely to support its survival.

But doesn't wildlife we *don't* know have the same right to survive?

Life links
Survival is about links and balance. In an aquarium, fish, snails and pond plants survive if their numbers are in balance.

Adding fish or snails upsets the balance, by increasing competition for space, food, mates or oxygen. Removing fish, snails or pond plants upsets the balance by reducing the availability of food, oxygen producers or breeding partners.

Links between species can be obscure:

In Africa, there are trees threatened with extinction because there are no elephants to eat their fruits and distribute their seeds in the dung.

In Central America, trees that relied on giant sloths to spread their seeds nearly became extinct when man killed the sloths. Luckily, horses of incoming Europeans took over the sloths' role of seed dispersers.

Rodent rage
Being unaware of these links can bring problems when we alter a habitat's wildlife. In isolated communities, like islands, small changes can produce big results.
- On Bird Island, in the Seychelles, rats escaped from a ship and promptly ate the eggs and young of the local ground-nesting sooty terns.
- In New Zealand, the arrival of rats has caused serious loss of biodiversity. One of the world's rarest birds, the Raratonga flycatcher, which survives on the Cook Islands, has only been saved from extinction by positive rat control.

Introducing trouble
Wildlife has been introduced without affecting local wildlife. The little owl (from continental Europe) has lived here successfully for many years.

The North American ruddy duck is a different story. It escaped from wildfowl collections in Britain, then spread abroad. In Spain, it breeds with the white-headed duck, a globally threatened species. Producing hybrid (cross-bred) ducks threatens 'pure' white-headed ducks with extinction.

Other introductions threaten to bring extinctions:
- New Zealand flatworms (brought in with pot plants) are eating our earthworms. If earthworms become extinct, soil structure will suffer and food for birds and mammals will be lost.
- American crayfish are driving our native crayfish from rivers and streams.

Biodiversity brings added value
Oceans are fished and forests felled because fish and timber have commercial value. To keep that value, fishing and felling must be sustainable. This only happens if

oceans and forests keep their biodiversity. Extinction of part reduces the value of the whole.

Commercial forces must be controlled. When over-fishing wiped out huge shoals of North Sea herrings, the population of the herrings' prey, sandeels, boomed. So sandeels were fished instead.

Just when we should have been helping herring stocks rebuild, we were removing their food supply!

Off Labrador, the Grand Banks supported a huge cod-fishing industry on both sides of the Atlantic for over 200 years. Now over-fishing has almost entirely destroyed it.

Non-commercial species are valuable, too. They make holiday areas more attractive. 'Eco-tourists' travel to see local wildlife, not sparrows, crows and gulls they could see at home.

'Flagship' species can awaken interest in saving local habitats. Local awareness of wildlife makes accidental extinction less likely.

In St Lucia, parrots appear on flags, phone cards, postcards and even music labels, to keep wildlife in the minds of both locals and visitors.

In Scotland, the ospreys of Loch Garten do much the same, having become part of the local tourist industry.

Extinction is for life

- Extinction did not die out with the dinosaurs, it happens every day.
- Everything alive on Earth is part of the rich variety that makes our planet, as far as we know, unique in the universe.
- Who could watch even one species switch from 'endangered' to 'extinct'?

• The above is an extract from *6th Sense*, the magazine for students produced by the RSPB. See page 41 for address details.

© RSPB
Spring, 2000

The impact of man

Nature 'will take more than 10 million years' to recover from mankind

Life on earth will take at least 10 million years to recover from the mass extinction of animals and plants brought about by human activities, say scientists. An investigation of the ease with which life rebounds after a mass extinction has found that it takes far longer than previously realised.

Even if man survives for 2 million years – the average span for a typical mammal species – the Earth will still be suffering from his influence millions of years after he has become extinct.

Although there are now more living species on the planet than at any other single period in history, they are dying out at a faster rate than in any of the previous five mass extinctions over the past 600 million years, the most recent bringing an end to the dinosaurs 65 million years ago.

Scientists believe that human activity, ranging from the destruction of the rainforests to environmental pollution, is causing a wave of extinctions that is running 10,000 times faster than would occur naturally.

Two ecologists, James Kirchner of the University of California, Berkeley, and Anne Weil of Duke University in North Carolina, have discovered in their analysis of the

*By Steve Connor,
Science Editor*

five previous mass extinctions that recovery of species diversity took far longer than supposed.

'Our results suggest that there are intrinsic "speed limits" that regulate recovery from small extinctions as well as large ones,' they write in the journal *Nature*.

Even if man survives for 2 million years the Earth will still be suffering from his influence millions of years after he has become extinct

'Thus, today's anthropogenic extinctions are likely to have long-lasting effects, whether or not they are comparable in scope to the major mass extinctions,' they said.

'Even if *Homo sapiens* survives several million more years, it is unlikely that any of our species will see biodiversity recover from today's extinctions.'

Although 'background' extinctions occur all the time, mass extinctions – where tens of thousands of species are lost over a relatively short period – are believed to be related to cataclysmic environmental changes, such as massive volcanic eruptions or meteor strikes.

The researchers found that in the immediate aftermath of a mass extinction there is a serious depletion of the available ecological niches in which specialist animals and plants can live. This results in the so-called generalist species – such as cockroaches and rats – filling the gaps.

Douglas Erwin, a palaeobiologist at the National Museum of Natural History in Washington DC, said that during smaller extinctions niches can be refilled by species closely related to the ones lost. 'But larger extinctions seemingly cause a disappearance of the ecological fabric, which can only slowly be rebuilt,' he said.

Only a tiny fraction of the species that have died out over the past 500 years – such as the great auk and red macaw – have actually been recorded as extinct. Meanwhile, thousands of other animals, ranging from the white rhino and Sumatran tiger, to the giant tortoise and the golden lion tamarin, are on the endangered list. © *The Independent March, 2000*

British endangered species

Information from Care for the Wild International

What is an endangered species?

If a species is said to be endangered, then it is in danger of going extinct if the reasons that are causing its numbers to decline are not identified and the problems put right.

- Vulnerable species are those who are declining in numbers quite rapidly.
- Rare species are those which are only found in a particular area, or in a habitat that is found only in a few places in Britain.
- The term 'threatened' is used to describe species that are included in all these categories. This term is frequently used when talking about British species.

Why do species become threatened?

Different species are suited to different habitats or types of vegetation, they live where they find the other species that they feed on and where they are able to build their homes, and where they are able to protect their young. The numbers of many animal and plant species in Britain have declined in recent years due to the loss of the habitat in which they are usually found. Different habitat types are lost when we build on them to accommodate an increasing human population. Changes in the climate also affect some habitat types.

What can be done?

If we protect the habitats that threatened animal species are found in then they will also be protected. To do this, we need to identify the animals and plants that are declining by counting them, we need to see if they are found in all of the places that they used to be found, and we need to find out as much as is possible about their lives and what they need to live.

We need to ensure that habitats that have decreased in recent years are prevented from declining any further. We can do this by ensuring that they are not built on, by replanting trees where they have been cut down, by not polluting our waterways and by creating new areas of rare habitats. There are laws that help us to do this and the Government draws up guidelines with help from nature organisations to ensure that threatened species are protected to prevent them becoming extinct.

Some of the threatened species in Britain

In Britain we have lost over 100 species this century. Species that have not been recorded in Britain in the last 10 years include fish called sturgeon and houting, several species of beetles, a moth and several species of moss and lichen.

Recently species and habitats that are most threatened in Britain have been prioritised and species action plans have been written for them. The factors that are causing them to decline and what can be done to help them are included in these action plans.

Here are some examples of the species that are most threatened in Britain.

Mammals

Water vole (Arvicola terrestris)
The water vole is a small mammal similar in appearance to a mouse, it is found mainly in lowland areas near water. A recent population estimate suggested that the total British population was 1,200,000.

The water vole was once common and widespread throughout Britain but its habitat has become fragmented and has declined because of disturbance along our rivers. Pollution of waterways and accidental poisoning is also linked to the decline of water vole, as is predation by mink.

Ways of helping the water vole population include making sure that their habitat is not disturbed in the future, to avoid the use of pesticides near areas known to have water voles and to make sure that landowners know if they have them on their land and what they can do to help them.

European otter (Lutra lutra)
The European otter is a semi-aquatic mammal that feeds mainly on fish. The number of otters in the United Kingdom has declined a lot since the 1950s and the species was lost from many areas by 1980. They can now be found in Wales, SE England and much of Scotland. The otter is protected by several agreements between the UK and other countries that also have populations.

The numbers have declined because of pollution in waterways, this also reduces the amount of available food for them. Sites where the otters can breed and rest have declined, and they are also sometimes accidentally killed on the roads and in fish traps.

There have been lots of surveys of otters and some riverside areas have been especially designed for their needs. This is done by ensuring that they are surrounded by deciduous trees and shrubs and other types of habitat that otters require. It may also include creating log piles and artificial holts (breeding nests).

Bechstein's bat (Myotis bechsteinii)

There are 14 species of bats living in the British Isles, all of which are protected by law. Bat species are particularly threatened because they require safe places for them to hibernate and to sleep. Many species roost in old hollow trees, the number of these has declined a lot over recent years, increasingly forcing bats to roost in old buildings. Here they may be disturbed, their access holes may be blocked up accidentally and they are badly affected if woodwork in the building is treated with chemicals for woodworm.

Bats are difficult to study and they reproduce at a low rate. Bechstein's bat is one of the rarest species, it is a tree-dwelling species preferring broad-leaved woodland. There are only thought to be around 1,500 individuals left in the UK.

There are many specialist bat groups around Britain who are actively involved with bat conservation. Known hibernation sites have been protected against disturbance and bat boxes have been provided in areas where roost sites are limited.

Birds

Marsh warbler (Acrocephalus palustris)

The marsh warbler comes to Britain in the summer to breed. In 1980 there were thought to be 50-80 pairs. During the 1980s what was thought to be the main population, which was found in Worcestershire and the Severn and Avon valleys, declined rapidly and none were recorded there in 1989. A population was established in Kent in the 1970s which is thought to have over 25 pairs and there are now also several other pairs thought to breed in surrounding counties. There are also populations of this species in other European countries.

Changes in vegetation type are thought to be responsible for the decline of the Avon valley population. Changes in the climate are thought to have affected the species as a whole. Also, the populations of this species have become quite fragmented – they are found only in a few areas – this makes it difficult for different birds to meet. Disturbance by bird watchers and people along rivers also affects how well the birds breed.

Action to help to conserve the marsh warbler is being carried out by wildlife trusts and conservation organisations in areas known to have populations at present, and in areas that used to have populations. They monitor the number of birds that are present, they work to increase the amount and types of habitat that the species needs and try to reduce disturbance of the nests.

Nightjar (Caprimulgus europaeus)

The nightjar is also a summer migrant, its numbers and places where it can be found have both declined during the last 100 years. In 1992 there were thought to be 3,400 males coming to Britain, they are mainly found in southern England but there are some populations as far north as Scotland. The species has also declined in Europe.

The most important British habitats for this species are lowland heathland and young forestry plantations. Heathland in the UK has declined as more land is used for farming and building development. Cultivated land is not suitable habitat for the birds as it does not support many of the big insects that the nightjar likes to feed on. The nightjar nests in new plantations where there are still spaces of bare ground between the trees.

The nightjar has several laws that protect it and conservation initiatives work towards maintaining the different habitat types that they require.

Amphibians

Natterjack toad (Bufo calamita)

The natterjack toad is the rarest amphibian species native to Britain. It can be found at 4 natural sites in Scotland and 35 in England. In order to help its conservation it has also been introduced into 13 further sites.

Like other toads it lives most of its life on land, in holes beneath tree roots or in hedges, but returns to ponds to breed. It is found in heathland, sand dunes and saltmarsh habitats, but it has declined as the amount of these habitats has declined. It also suffers when the pools that it spawns in are polluted. Toads are also at risk from predation and being run over.

During the summer they shed their skins several times and they hibernate in October and November. When they emerge in March or April they make their way back to the pond where they were born. This makes it very important to conserve its habitat and to know exactly where any members of this species are present.

Plants

Lady's slipper orchid (Cypripedium calceolus)

There are 54 species of orchid that grow in Britain. Many of these species are rare, but their seeds are so light that the wind can carry them hundreds of miles so they are often found in many different places in small numbers. Development of orchids is very slow, it can take years for them to grow large enough for them to flower. This characteristic makes orchids very vulnerable as any decline in numbers would take a long time to recover.

The lady's slipper orchid grows on limestone grassland that is only moderately grazed by sheep and cows. The species has suffered a severe decline and only naturally occurs at one site, although the colony is growing.

The species has declined due to people picking them and trampling on them, as well as their surrounding habitat being destroyed by too much grazing.

The species is protected by law and the site where it is found is subject to careful habitat management and wardening. There is also work going on to introduce the plant to other areas. These may be areas where it used to be found, if the habitat is still suitable, or new areas that have all of the characteristics it requires. It is hoped that by 2004 populations of the species will be found at 5 sites.

© Care for the Wild International (CFTWI)

Endangered British mammals

Britain has a rich heritage of wild mammals, yet many are disappearing from our countryside and coastlines. This article describes the threats facing British mammals and the action that needs to be taken to help save them.

Our mammal heritage

There are at least 69 species of wild mammals living in and around Britain and another 29 migratory species (bats and marine mammals), which occasionally visit. After the last ice age, 15,000 years ago, our native mammals crossed the land bridge attaching us to the continent. Some have already become extinct, including the beaver, brown bear and wolf. Others have been introduced to Britain by humans. The result is a unique mixture of species which forms our mammal heritage.

Britain and Ireland have two-thirds of the world's grey seals, probably half of Europe's otters and important populations of badgers, horseshoe bats and wildcats. These species are gone or on the brink of extinction in much of Europe so conserving them here is essential. Mammals are vital for the survival of other species. For example, the endangered barn owl feeds almost entirely on small mammals and will only thrive where they are abundant. Mammals indicate that our own local environment is healthy. The survival of otters and water voles means that our drinking water is clean.

Mammals are a familiar part of our culture. Millions have enjoyed the evocative tale of Mole, Ratty and Badger in *Wind in the Willows*, the dormouse and hare at Alice's tea party in Wonderland and the rabbits of *Watership Down*. Place names like Catford in London (a Saxon 'Wildcat ford') and Wolf Hill behind Belfast City are reminders that mammals are a mainstay of our wildlife heritage. Yet despite this familarity, few people regularly see wild mammals.

Which mammals need help?

- The otter was widespread in the 1950s but just twenty years later had disappeared from most of England and Wales. Only now are conservation measures beginning to reverse the decline.
- The dormouse has disappeared from half the range it was present in during the last century.
- The red squirrel is extinct over most of England and Wales.
- Bats. Populations of the 14 species which breed in Britain have all declined in recent decades. Pipistrelle numbers fell by 60% between 1978 and 1986. Greater and lesser horseshoe bats are endangered, the barbastelle is very poorly known and the mouse-eared bat became extinct in 1991.
- The water vole is suffering from a major long-term decline.
- The pine marten, once found within 30 miles of London, is now largely confined to remote areas in Scotland.
- The wildcat was once found throughout mainland Britain but is now confined to parts of Scotland.
- The polecat was once widespread but is now extinct in Scotland and most of England. Fortunately it is on the increase in Wales and the adjacent English counties.
- The brown hare is showing signs of a general decline.
- The mountain hare is locally vulnerable, especially the isolated, small (and only) English population in the Peak District.
- The common seal population has declined since the 1988 outbreak of phocine distemper.
- Whales, dolphins and porpoises are all less common off our coasts.

Why are mammals in danger?

Habitat destruction and isolation

Loss of ancient woodlands, hedge-rows, riverbank vegetation and wetlands has led to the loss of the mammals that live in these places. The remaining patches are often isolated and the mammals within them are at risk from local extinctions. Once a species is lost from an isolated habitat, recolonisation is often very difficult, perhaps impossible.

Changing land use

Mammals require diverse habitats with a range of food sources present throughout the year. In the past, traditional management of the countryside produced a patchwork of small fields and woodland which well suited mammals. Modern

... NEVER KNEW THERE WERE ANY LEFT IN THESE PARTS...

intensive agricultural methods and changes in land management severely reduce this diversity.

Poisoning and pollution

Pesticides accumulate in the bodies of otters and other predators at the top of the food chain. Water pollution threatens water voles, seals and marine mammals. PCBs from industrial sources affect reproduction and the immune system at minute concentrations.

Persecution

In the past, gamekeeping has driven many of our carnivores to the brink of extinction. Enlightened estate management and legal protection is helping to reverse this trend, but many endangered mammals are still being trapped, caught in snares or killed by poisoned bait.

Accidental killing or disturbance

Mammals are frequent road casualties. The impact on their population is unknown but likely to be heavy. Marine mammals drown when they become entangled in fishing nets set to catch other species. Sea and land mammals are both threatened by disturbance from people.

Introduction of non-native mammals

Our native mammals are vulnerable to predation, interbreeding and direct competition with species of mammals that have been introduced to Britain. This has led to near extinction of the red squrrrel, genetic dilution of the red deer and serious loss of water voles to imported mink.

What action is required?

To safeguard the future of Britain's mammals, we need to:
- Study and understand the reasons for decline in the numbers and distribution of British mammals. Long-term monitoring is vital.
- Protect key habitats, ensure appropriate habitat management and encourage less intensive farming.
- Reintroduce certain species, but only where there is good reason to expect success.
- Encourage the use of mammal-friendly pesticides and monitor threats from pollution and poisoning.
- Raise awareness of mammals and overcome prejudices against them.

• The Mammal Society is dedicated to promoting the study and conservation of British mammals. Membership is open to anyone with an interest in mammals. Mammal enthusiasts under 18 can join the Youth Group, Mammalaction. For details of membership or publications please write to The Mammal Society, at the address shown on page 41.

Threatened British wildlife and habitats

Britain's wildlife and their habitats have suffered large-scale losses and damage since the 1940s. The main causes have been intensive farming, road, housing and industrial developments, pollution, over-exploitation – especially of fisheries, commercial forestry and introduced species. Climate change is a more recently recognised threat which is likely to put our wildlife and habitats increasingly at risk in the future.

Modern technology has given us the tools to exploit Britain's resources as never before. The material benefits have been enormous, but the environmental costs have been high. We have enlarged and mechanised our farms and increased their yield by the use of fertilisers and pesticides. We have built towns, cities and roads, drained wetlands and reclaimed estuaries. Yet in doing all this we are little by little eroding the diversity and richness of our wildlife and reducing our choices for the future.

There are dozens of species which are endemic to the UK, that is they are found nowhere else. Many of these are severely threatened. When a species becomes extinct throughout its range it is gone for ever. This is why we have a special responsibility for our endemic species.

Wildlife habitat loss in post-war Britain

Dozens more species which occur in the UK and other countries are also threatened with world extinction. The UK must play a part in the international effort to maintain these species on Earth. Many species occur in the UK in internationally significant numbers, in other words, Britain holds a large proportion of the world or European population and has a particular responsibility to ensure these species are conserved. These species include the grey seal, for which the UK holds more than half the world population; and the gannet, 60 per cent of which breed in the UK.

What you can do

You can play your part in helping to ensure that wildlife can thrive by:

In the garden
- planting native wildflower seeds
- putting up a bird table, bird box, or bat box
- growing plants that attract butterflies
- getting a corner of the garden ready in October for hibernating animals such as hedgehogs or frogs
- using alternatives to peat (a natural habitat that cannot be renewed)
- avoiding pesticides altogether and trying biological pest control instead
- starting a compost heap
- choosing independently certified organic fertilisers

In the countryside
- taking all your rubbish home,

recycling what you can and cutting up and binning any plastic multi-pack can holders. Hundreds of birds and animals get caught up in them and die every year.

- not picking or digging up wild plants.

- respecting wildlife in ponds, streams and coastal rockpools.
- keeping to proper tracks and paths when out walking or cycling. Straying off marked paths could disturb or destroy wildlife.
- avoiding disturbance to marine life in water sports. Find out where

there are any particularly sensitive areas you should avoid.

- The above is an extract from *Threatened British wildlife and habitats*, produced by WWF-UK. See page 41 for address details.

Our countryside at risk

Information from Friends of the Earth

The UK's endangered wildlife

The British Isles support an amazing diversity of wildlife. Rich in wetlands, peatlands, grasslands, heaths, centuries-old woodlands, we have one of the most dramatic coastlines in the world. The UK is home to thousands of wild species: the wild cat, red kite, adonis blue butterfly, black poplar, grey seal and the harbour porpoise for example.

But all this is at risk. Our wildlife wealth is being traded for the short-term profit of developers, farmers and industrialists. Indeed most of the country's natural habitats have already gone.

We are left with a few islands of beauty in a sea of intensive agriculture, urban sprawl and degraded countryside. These are the green lungs in our choking, over-heated, polluted environment.

This article is a celebration of our most important wildlife habitats. We think everyone should know about and value these places; the information provided is intended to assist. It is also a call to arms to protect them from the overwhelming threats which make their future, and therefore the environment of our children, so uncertain. As far ago as 1990 William Wilkinson, former head of the Nature Conservancy Council, stated:

'To achieve success, nature conservation has to win the hearts and the interest of people throughout our land. To achieve success local enthusiasm will need to be harnessed to an effort of national will. It is a protective chain which we must forge around our land; if any link in it fails, the chain itself will snap.'

How our countryside has changed

As humans colonised the British Isles they changed the landscape by hunting the large grazing animals and transforming the UK's wild woodlands and wetlands into farmland. This has profoundly changed the distribution and diversity of species and habitat types throughout these islands. Many charismatic species that were once common in the UK have now been lost because they did not exist comfortably alongside humans: bear, wolf, beaver, lynx, wild cattle, wild horses, storks and bustards are among the casualties.

Some human impacts, however, have not been disastrous. Grazing with cattle or sheep can be similar to grazing by bison and coppicing woodlands acts like the wind blowing down trees and browsing by deer. Thus we have inherited a 'semi-natural' landscape where natural communities of species can exist within habitats that are managed in one way or another by humans.

This inheritance of semi-natural landscapes shows how harmonious our relationship with the natural world can be. Wildlife thrives in this environment and we can still appreciate how rich in wildlife our countryside must have been just a

Our wildlife wealth is being traded for the short-term profit of developers, farmers and industrialists

few generations ago by looking at our SSSIs, our best remaining wild places.

The industrial revolution and agricultural 'improvement', however, have consigned this sustainable landscape to just a few per cent of the UK. The small-scale peat cutting of generations of people living near Thorne Moor in North Lincolnshire, for example, is very different to the industrial-scale milling and draining by Levingtons which has cleared thousands of tonnes of peat from this internationally important SSSI in just a few short years, wiping out the wildlife on the site for the benefit of horticultural and garden peat.

Changes to agriculture have led to draining and ploughing of grasslands and wetlands, the conversion of colourful meadows rich in flowers to drab monocultures of wheat and rape and the removal of woodlands and hedgerows to make way for prairie fields laced with pesticides and chemical fertilisers.

The isolation of our wildlife

In 1637 the East Anglian fens covered 3,380 square kilometres. By 1984 they had been reduced to just 10 square kilometres. On the way the marsh harrier, bittern and large copper butterfly have all but disappeared. Many of the remaining patches are SSSIs.

Such small patches are extremely vulnerable to local disasters like fires, disease outbreaks, bad winters or droughts, all of which can wipe out isolated populations of rare species. In sites surrounded by wildlife-free zones of intensive agriculture, no prospect for re-colonisation exists and isolated areas of habitat can therefore enter a decline until their wildlife interest has gone.

The Institute of Terrestrial Ecology published a survey in 1990 indicating that over the previous six years the number of species found in woodlands declined by 14 per cent and in semi-improved grasslands by 13 per cent. Without action to improve conditions for wildlife in the wider countryside such declines in species-richness are inevitable inside SSSIs.

Protecting the wider countryside

We cannot ensure future generations will have a wildlife-rich environment to enjoy just by improving the legal protection of SSSIs. Wildlife does not exist in a bubble remote from the wider threats to our environment. We must tackle the threats leading to the destruction of SSSIs and therefore to the whole of our countryside. This means changing our own behaviour by building fewer roads and using our cars less, saving energy and water in the home, consuming less so more pollution is not pumped into the atmosphere and less material is mined from the land or seabed, reducing our waste and choosing to buy our food from those who farm organically rather than with damaging chemicals.

Land outside SSSIs is just as under threat. SSSIs are mainly designated for their habitats with the result that most of our rarest species live outside the protected sites. Above all, these species are influenced by agricultural policy and in particular the Common Agricultural Policy drawn up in Europe and largely responsible for the destruction of our countryside.

Successive governments have failed to stand up for the UK's wildlife and change the Common Agricultural Policy, opting instead to support the interests of a few wealthy 'barley barons' and see our wildlife wiped out. Despite the rhetoric of political parties for change to these damaging policies, little of substance has changed and the Ministry of Agriculture still pays farmers huge sums of taxpayers' money to destroy wildlife sites.

The 1992 Earth Summit in Rio committed governments through international law to conserving the diversity of species, habitats and genes on the planet through the Convention on Biological Diversity. As a result the Government has adopted a set of Biodiversity Action Plans (BAPs) to reverse the declines in our most endangered species and habitats. By the end of 1999 over 400 plans for species and 40 for habitat types had been prepared with more under way.

The process of compiling and adopting these plans has been successful and is to be commended, however, it has been achieved through a voluntary process with no basis in UK law. Friends of the Earth believes the targets in these ambitious plans will not be achieved unless the Biodiversity Action Plan process is placed on a statutory footing. The reasons for this are several. In the first instance, where conflict arises, ministers will be unable to make decisions in favour of biodiversity unless they have statutory powers to do so, at least, not without risking legal challenge. In addition only a legal framework for the process will allow it to be correctly prioritised across all levels of government. Finally the Government intends to fulfil some of its legal statutory obligations under the Habitats Directive through the, at present, *voluntary* BAP process. Clearly this is unsatisfactory.

The scale of habitat loss

In just a few short decades our countryside has been ploughed and drained by farmers, poisoned with pollution by industry, covered with Tarmac and concrete by planners and developers, robbed of water by water companies and turned into a tamed and packaged heritage attraction for motoring holiday makers. Most of our habitats have declined drastically. For some, according to the forerunner of today's conservation agencies the Nature Conservancy Council, 'the scale and rate have been catastrophic'. The following are estimates of habitat loss since 1945 made by the Government's conservation agencies and other organisations:

- Ancient woodland: 30-50 per cent loss;
- Flower-rich meadows: 95 per cent loss;
- Lowland grasslands on chalk and limestone: 80 per cent loss or significant damage;
- Lowland heath: 60 per cent loss;
- Limestone pavements in northern England: 45 per cent badly damaged or destroyed. Only 3 per cent left untouched;
- Fens and coastal marshes: 50 per cent loss or significant damage;
- Lowland raised bogs: 94 per cent loss or significant damage;
- Upland grasslands, heaths and blanket bogs: 30 per cent loss or significant damage;
- Hedgerows: by 1974, 140,000 miles of hedgerow had been removed (from a total of 500,000 in 1946-47);
- Estuaries: over 65 per cent of our estuaries are under threat.

With the loss of habitat there has been a drastic decline in species such as the early gentian, stone curlew and silver-spotted skipper.

© Friends of the Earth

A green and pleasant land?

Sadly, not for mammals. Information from the Mammal Society

- Over 50,000 badgers are killed on the roads each year.
- In just 20 years three-quarters of all known harvest mouse colonies disappeared following clearance of the areas of long grass they need to build their nests.
- Chemical, noise and rubbish pollution, disturbance, propeller injuries and net entanglement all threaten bottle-nosed dolphins in British waters.
- A third of stoats, weasels and polecats carry significant levels of rodenticides from eating contaminated prey; the effect on these carnivores is unknown.
- Removal of old trees reduces the numbers of roost sites for bats.
- Brown hares have declined by 80% this century as a result of increasing agricultural intensification.
- Red squirrels have virtually disappeared from England and Wales following the introduction of grey squirrels.
- Many patches of woodland are now too small to hold dormice and their numbers have declined dramatically this century.

Britain's wild mammals are some of the most beautiful on Earth and are an important indicator of the health of our environment. But many are under serious threat.

We desperately need to improve our understanding of how and where they live and the threats they face to develop scientifically based policies to protect them. This is where the Mammal Society comes in.

The Mammal Society works to protect British mammals, halt the decline of threatened species, and advise on all issues affecting British mammals. We study mammals, identify problems they face and promote conservation and other policies based on sound science.

Specifically, the Mammal Society seeks to:

- Raise awareness of mammals, their ecology and their conservation needs
- Survey British mammals and their habitats to identify the threats they face
- Promote mammal studies in the UK and overseas
- Advocate conservation plans based on sound science
- Provide current information on mammals through our publications
- Involve people of all ages in our efforts to protect mammals
- Educate people about British mammals
- Monitor mammal population changes.

But we need your support to continue with this crucial work.

- For details on how to join the Mammal Society, please contact them at 15 Cloisters House, 8 Battersea Park Road, London SW8 4BG. Tel: 020 7498 5358 Fax: 020 7622 8722. Alternatively you can e-mail them at enquiries@mammal.org.uk or visit their web site at www.mammal.org.uk

© The Mammal Society

Charity's plea to save rare plants

Conservationists today launch an appeal to save Britain's rarest plants, including camomile, cornflower and early gentian, after a Government scheme failed to find business sponsors.

The appeal is being led by the charity Plantlife, which has been given responsibility by English Nature, the Government's conservation advisers, for saving 72 of the most endangered plants. It is launched as the National Trust calls for 50 per cent of agricultural subsidies – around £1.5 billion a year – to be diverted to support nature conservation.

Plantlife warns that unless funds are provided for endangered species to be surveyed and their habitats restored, the plants could join the 107 British species which have become extinct this century. Eight species of flowering plant have died out since 1970, including the spectacular summer lady's tresses, an orchid once found in the New Forest and the Channel Islands. It fell victim to collecting and land drainage.

Martin Harper, director of conservation at Plantlife, said the charity was reporting to the Government and English Nature on progress with Britain's biodiversity action plans – the recovery plans for rare species. 'We are appealing to the public for help because we are not getting it from industry,' he said.

Twenty-five corporate 'champions' had been found for some of the more than 350 endangered British species listed as a requirement of the Biodiversity Convention signed at the 1992 Rio Earth Summit.

ICI is the corporate 'champion' for the large blue butterfly and Tesco has adopted the skylark. But Plantlife has had difficulty finding sponsors for plants. Wessex Water funded a booklet on the early gentian, a plant unique to Britain, but the sole plant 'champion' is Center Parcs, which is sponsoring eight species.

The National Trust will call for a massive switch of farm subsidies from price support and production subsidies into environmental schemes at a conference in London today.

A spokesman said that schemes allowing farmers to develop the wildlife potential of the countryside were a vital defence against falling prices for produce.

© Telegraph Group Limited, London 2000

Lowest ebb on record for many UK birds

Several familiar countryside birds, including song thrushes, grey partridges and corn buntings, have fallen to their lowest recorded numbers, according to a new report from the RSPB and the British Trust for Ornithology.

The State of the UK Birds, which examines the falling and rising populations of the UK's regular breeding birds between 1970 and 1999, also reveals that three-quarters of the Government's much-publicised biodiversity action plans, created to reverse declining bird populations, have little hope of reaching their short- or medium-term targets, and further population declines are inevitable.

Dr Mark Avery, the RSPB's director of conservation, said: 'Currently, only a handful of the Government's 26 biodiversity action plans for birds are likely to reach or exceed their targets. Generally, the most successful action plans are for the rarer species in the UK, including corncrake, cirl bunting and stone-curlew, where targeted on-the-ground action can deliver immediate benefits, largely thanks to wildlife-friendly landowners and conservation groups.

'To date the bulk of plans for more widely dispersed birds have largely been unsuccessful. This is simply because the action plans' recommendations, such as greater funding for wildlife-friendly farming, have not yet been implemented on a large enough scale at a national or European level. These birds will continue to fall in number until we have the necessary changes in policy.'

Dr Jeremy Greenwood, director of the British Trust for Ornithology, said: 'It is not only farmland birds that are suffering. Our volunteers, who provide the bulk of the observations on which our results are based, survey all the main habitats in Britain. As a result, we know there have been worrying losses among several woodland species, such as marsh tit, willow tit and redpoll.

'Even some familiar urban birds, such as starlings and house sparrows, have undergone dramatic declines. All are candidates for addition to the nation's set of Biodiversity Action Plans.'

Although the downward population trends continue for 44 species of widespread bird in the UK, the *State of the UK Birds* report also highlights spectacular conservation successes, including the red kite, osprey and marsh harrier, birds of prey which have all more than doubled their UK populations since 1970, thanks to reduced persecution, the increased management of nature reserves, the banning of organo-chlorine pesticides and reintro-duction schemes for red kite.

Other species with notably rising UK populations include the blackcap, nuthatch and great spotted woodpecker, some of which are believed to be benefiting from milder winters, possibly as a result of climate change. Over the last three decades nuthatches and great spotted woodpeckers have continued to expand their ranges northwards into Scotland.

Dr David Gibbons, head of the RSPB's conservation science department, said: 'The report notes there are nearly 40 more bird species breeding in the UK at the end of the 20th century than at the beginning of the 19th.

'One-third of these species, including the golden pheasant, the mandarin duck and the ring-necked parakeet, have been introduced by people but the remainder, including Cetti's warbler, collared dove and goldeneye, have colonised naturally. In the last 30 years there has been a net increase of four species per decade, with the little egret colonising as recently as 1996.'

• Copies of *State of the UK's Birds* are available free of charge from: RSPB, The Lodge, Sandy, Bedfordshire SG19 2DL. It can also be found on the RSPB's website via the homepage www.rspb.org.uk

© RSPB
February, 2000

Species action programme

Towards recovery for Scotland's threatened wildlife

Why is conservation action needed?

As a result of human pressures much of Scotland's wildlife has declined markedly or is threatened with extinction. Many of the populations that still survive are now small and may no longer be viable. Often they are isolated in increasingly fragmented landscapes.

For these threatened species, legal protection or even the conservation of their habitat may not be enough to maintain existing populations or permit their expansion to new or former localities. In these circumstances, direct intervention may be required if we hope to retain them as components of our natural heritage.

Where species threatened with extinction are endemic to Scotland, that is they occur nowhere else in the world, lack of action on our part may lead to their extinction on a global scale. In other cases, conservation efforts here may have international significance if the species is also threatened elsewhere or if we hold a significant proportion of the world population.

How is action determined?

Before we can take direct action for a species we must know how abundant and widely distributed they are so that any change in their status can be assessed. The reasons for change need to be understood if they are to be rectified. Research may need to be carried out to establish the key requirements for the species so that future management can be guided. Increasingly this work is aimed at the production of a 'Species Action Plan' in which targets are set for recovery and the means to achieve these are indicated.

Positive action for a species might include restoring favourable conditions or the provision of breeding sites. Where a species no longer occurs in a former locality and there is no prospect of it re-

establishing itself, then reintroduction may be considered. Proposals are assessed carefully against criteria produced by the International Union for the Conservation of Nature (IUCN).

What action is SNH taking?

SNH and its predecessors have long been involved with recovery work for our threatened wildlife. Existing projects include the reintroduction of red kites and sea-eagles to Scotland and participation in the Corncrake Initiative. Habitat management has been undertaken to restore viability to the only surviving colony of New Forest burnet moths in the British Isles and breeding pools have been created to maintain vulnerable colonies of natterjack toads on the Solway coast.

Species action plans and recovery work have also been identified by the Government as key tasks in our contribution to the conservation of biodiversity, the variety of plants and animals. *Biodiversity: the UK Action Plan* identifies the priorities for future work on species.

The SNH Species Action Programme provides a co-ordinated approach to the recovery of our priority species. We aim to maintain or restore viable populations of such threatened wildlife across their traditional range by taking appropriate positive action. SNH cannot undertake this work alone, but needs to work in partnership with others such as voluntary bodies, researchers, land managers and zoological and botanical gardens.

SNH Species Action Programme is co-ordinated by the International and Biodiversity Branch of our Research and Advisory Services Directorate.

Scottish Natural Heritage

Scottish Natural Heritage is a government body responsible to the Scottish Executive and Scottish Parliament.

Our mission statement is:
Working with Scotland's people to care for our natural heritage.

Our aim is:
Scotland's natural heritage is a local, national and global asset. We promote its care and improvement, its responsible enjoyment, its greater understanding and appreciation and its sustainable use now and for future generations.

Beavers make a comeback in Scotland

*By Auslan Cramb,
Scotland Correspondent*

The European beaver, hunted to extinction at least 400 years ago, is to become the first mammal to be reintroduced to Britain. Around 12 animals will be released on a Scottish river system within the next two years.

The return of the herbivorous rodent received overwhelming public support in a poll, but has been criticised by landowners who fear it will damage salmon spawning grounds.

Detailed studies of river habitats suggested that up to 1,000 beavers could survive on the rivers Ness, Spey, Tay, Dee, Don and Lomond. But Scottish Natural Heritage, the Government environment agency, agreed yesterday to limit the re-introduction initially to a single site on land owned by the Forestry Commission. The 'reversible pilot project', in the north or west of Scotland, will last seven years, and will be used to test concerns about the animal's return.

SNH is also prepared to cancel the reintroduction and shoot the beavers 'as a last resort' if they cause severe environmental damage. Most conservationists are confident that the experiment will succeed and see the return of the large rodents as a symbol of the ecological recovery of Scottish river systems.

In its evidence to SNH, the World Wide Fund for Nature said the otter, water vole, trout and salmon could all benefit from beavers' coppicing of trees, small-scale dam building and grazing of aquatic vegetation.

A spokesman for SNH said that the European beaver, unlike its larger American cousin, did not build huge dams, and had been successfully reintroduced to 14 other European countries. Its return was approved at a meeting in Perth after what one source described as 'last-minute nerves'. The cost of the scheme will be around £400,000, with SNH supplying half that amount. It hopes the balance will come from other interested agencies, wildlife charities and donations. Two or three family groups of beavers will be trapped in Norway and released in the High-lands in 2002. They will be radio tagged, and will be returned to the chosen site if they venture too far down river.

Jeremy Read, director of the Atlantic Salmon Trust, welcomed the measures to control the project,

but expressed disappointment at the reintroduction. He said: 'It sounds as if it is being approached in a responsible way, but we can't be enthusiastic. The salmon is in a difficult enough state at the moment without any additional potential hazards.'

Malcolm Borthwick, a retired farmer and member of the Scottish Landowners' Federation, said: 'History is littered with introductions of things that society has come to regret.' He predicted that the move would prove 'expensive and fool-hardy' and said SNH should have adopted the precautionary principle and delayed the reintroduction until Scottish salmon stocks had recovered.

News of the beaver's reintroduction follows the successful return of the sea eagle and the red kite. The European beaver eats grasses and herbs in the summer, and switches to the bark of broad-leaved trees in autumn and winter, although wildlife experts say it will not damage conifer plantations.

In medieval times, beavers were hunted for their fur and scent glands, which were used in medicine and perfume. There was a thriving beaver-trapping industry in Inverness, but by 1188 they could be found only on the River Dee, in north-east Scotland, and they were persecuted to extinction by the end of the 16th century.

There are no plans to re-introduce the beaver in England in the near future.

*© Telegraph Group Limited,
London 2000*

Wildlife trade in the UK

Information from TRAFFIC

The global trade in wild plants and animals and their products is enormous, with an annual turnover of billions of pounds.

The UK is one of the more significant wildlife consuming nations in the world. Trade occurs in a variety of mammals, birds, reptiles, insects, frogs and plants as well as in their products and derivatives. The species in trade include both native and exotic plants and animals.

The trade in exotic species as pets in particular is flourishing, especially in reptiles and amphibians. Iguanas are the most commonly traded exotic reptiles. A single legal shipment of Green Iguana *Iguana iguana* entering the UK can contain 2000-5000 iguanas. Boas, pythons, chameleons and geckos are frequently imported and traded privately and in pet shops. The UK imports more than one million live reptiles and amphibians annually.

Other exotic wildlife commonly featured in the UK pet trade include birds and tropical fish. Bird keeping has long been popular and exotic parrots and finches are traded in large numbers. Falconry in particular has steadily increased. The tropical fish and aquarium trade is also very large but it is mostly unregulated and therefore the extent of trade is difficult to quantify.

Stuffed animals, both native and exotic, are favoured among collectors and the taxidermy trade is widespread. There has also been a dramatic increase in recent years in the use of traditional and herbal medicines, frequently containing wild plant and animal derivatives.

In 1996, the most recent year for which complete data is available, the UK legally imported tens of thousands of live plants and animals and their derivatives regulated in international trade under the Convention on International Trade in Endangered Species of Wild Fauna and Flora (CITES). These included 16,000 birds, 3,000 plants, 25,000

reptiles and amphibians, and 2,800 mammals. During this same year, 90,000 pieces of reptile skins and 42,200 pieces of coral were also legally imported. An even greater number of non-CITES species are imported into the UK each year.

The increasing popularity of wildlife and wildlife products in the UK has been complemented by a growing number of laws and regulations aimed at controlling the trade to ensure its sustainability. However, while the majority of wildlife trade is legal, there is a persistent illegal trade, particularly in live wildlife such as exotic reptiles, native birds of prey and rare parrots. There is also a significant illegal trade in products derived from wildlife, such as ornaments, reptile skins, wool and fabric from wild mammals, foodstuffs and traditional medicines.

The most worrying trend of wildlife smuggling into the UK is the increasing phenomenon of wildlife being smuggled into other European Union countries with weaker border controls and then transported unimpeded into the UK. This trend has developed as a result of the establishment of the EU single market in 1993, which meant that special permits to import CITES-listed species are no longer required in the UK if these species are being imported from other EU member countries.

As in all countries, the secretive nature of illegal trade makes it impossible to accurately quantify. However, in the case of native birds of prey, illegal capture and sales in the UK have been frequent. The Peregrine Falcon *Falco Peregrinus* is the most targeted. Little more than 1,000 pairs are believed to remain in the wild in the UK. Butterflies are the most common native invertebrates found in illegal trade in the UK, while the trade – legal or illegal – in native reptiles and amphibians is minimal. A number of rare native orchids as well as wild bulbs such as snowdrops *Galanthus nivalis* are also illegally traded.

In regard to the scale of illegal trade in exotic species, in one recent year Customs officials made more than 30,000 seizures of CITES-listed plants and animals illegally entering the UK, according to the Department of Environment, Transport and the Regions (DETR), the government department responsible for management of wildlife trade in the UK. However, a great number of wildlife and wildlife products get past the enforcement net at the border and illegally enter the country, where they are then found in commercial trade.

In recent years, the UK Government has begun to invest more resources in combating wildlife crime in the UK, principally with the development of the Partnership for Action Against Wildlife Crime, the Police Wildlife Liaison Officer Network, specially designated Customs CITES liaison officers and the CITES Enforcement Teams based at Heathrow Airport and the port of Dover. Nonetheless, wildlife crime in the UK continues for a number of reasons, including the often light penalties handed down by the courts for wildlife trading offences. These inadequate penalties reflect a lack of awareness on the part of the judiciary about the seriousness of wildlife crimes.

© *TRAFFIC*

Operation Charm

Operation Charm is helping to protect wildlife by preventing the illegal trade in traditional Chinese medicines which contain bears and other endangered animals and plants. With your help we can stop this trade.

- Interpol estimate that the world-wide trade in endangered species is worth US$5 billion every year. This puts it second only to the illegal trade in drugs, in terms of its cash value.
- WWF say that at least one tiger is killed in the wild every day in order to meet the demand for traditional Chinese medicines.
- Ed Espinoza, the Deputy Director of the US Fish and Wildlife Service Forensic Laboratory, recently said: 'If 0.1 per cent of the Asian population earned enough to buy a single gall bladder then all of the bears in North America would be needed to supply that demand.'
- 96% of the world's population of black rhinos has disappeared since 1970 as a result of the demand for rhinoceros horn.

These are depressing facts which underline the sheer scale of the illegal international trade in endangered species and the threat which it poses to their survival.

Of course, most endangered species do not live in the wild in Britain, or even in Europe, yet the demand for them exists here, and in many cases, it is this demand for the body parts and derivatives of these animals which is the reason they are threatened with extinction on other continents.

Britain is a signatory to the Convention on International Trade in Endangered Species (CITES). CITES strictly controls or, in the case of the rarest species, bans the trade in endangered species, their body parts and derivatives. Nevertheless, Britain is a consumer of endangered species and police and HM Customs and Excise have an important role to play in enforcing the law and fighting the illegal trade. London is one of the principal points of entry to Europe, as well as being a major trading centre and endangered species from all over the world can, and do, turn up here.

Operation Charm is the Metropolitan Police initiative against the illegal trade in endangered species in London.

Since its launch in 1995 much of our work has concentrated on the trade in animals such as tigers, rhinos and bears, derivatives of which are used in some illegal traditional Chinese medicines (TCMs).

Operation Charm is the Metropolitan Police initiative against the illegal trade in endangered species in London

---

In February 1995 the Metropolitan Police executed search warrants at the premises of a number of Chinese pharmacies in central London, in response to evidence obtained by the wildlife trade monitoring organisation, TRAFFIC International. On the same day police in Manchester and Birmingham conducted similar searches and, between us, we seized several thousand illegal medicine products as well as raw materials (i.e. body parts) of tiger, rhino, bear and many other species.

Subsequently eight traders were convicted in the courts and one of these has also been the subject of disciplinary action by his professional body.

In London we continued to gather evidence on the illegal TCM trade, and this has led to further searches and seizures at the premises of importers and retailers in the London area. Prosecutions are pending in most of these cases although some minor offenders have been dealt with by formal cautions. This is a procedure by which minor offenders can be cautioned by police, where an offence is not contested, rather than going through a prosecution.

In August 1996 the Metropolitan Police hosted a seminar of TCM practitioners and traders with a view to explaining the law protecting endangered species in the UK, and the reasons for the law, as well as looking at ways in which we can work together to prevent the illegal trade. At the seminar we launched a 'sticker scheme' by which any TCM trader who signs a simple undertaking stating that they will not knowingly trade in endangered species can obtain a Metropolitan Police window sticker which shows their commitment to trade lawfully, and this can be displayed at their premises. The sticker scheme has been very successful and, so far, around 100 traders have joined.

In 1997 Esso UK Plc showed their support for Operation Charm by providing funding for the publication of an advice leaflet for TCM traders. This has been produced in English and Chinese and has been widely distributed to traders in the London area.

The growing Western interest in TCM has led to a big increase in the number of TCM traders in London and it is important that Operation Charm is developed further in future. The majority of traders in London do not knowingly trade in endangered species, but others continue to do so. In future, we will continue to take enforcement action where this is appropriate but we also intend to continue to work with TCM traders to prevent the illegal trade. The seminar, sticker scheme and advice leaflet are examples of partnership initiatives which we have introduced so far. These have shown a willingness amongst traders to carry out their business lawfully, and we have received the very valuable support of some prominent TCM traders within the Chinese community.

In 1997 the Register of Chinese Herbal Medicine (a London-based professional body) joined forces with the wildlife conservation organisation, Tusk Force, to lobby the British Government for greater regulation of the TCM trade in the UK, including the setting of minimum standards for practitioners. These standards would include strict compliance with CITES Regulations.

Another important aspect of Operation Charm is to raise the level of public awareness of the illegal trade in endangered species here in Britain. Many people here are well aware of the threat to endangered species like the tiger, but few realise that there is an illegal trade in them here. We have taken a number of initiatives to increase public awareness of this including publication of the leaflet *Protecting Endangered Species*, as well as posters and the first in a series of postcards on the issue.

However, Operation Charm is not just looking into the TCM trade. Endangered species are traded illegally in London, in many different forms, and this has been illustrated

---

These are depressing facts which underline the sheer scale of the illegal international trade in endangered species and the threat which it poses to their survival

---

by some of the seizures we have made. These have included live reptiles, elephant ivory and Shahtoosh shawls. Shahtoosh is the wool of the endangered Chiru, or Tibetan antelope, and is the finest wool known to man. Traditionally, this has been used in the manufacture of shawls which sell for very high prices in Indian communities in many different countries. The animals have to be killed and skinned in order to obtain the wool and, as the Chiru is included in Appendix I of CITES, all trade in the species or its derivatives is banned.

In February 1997 Metropolitan Police Wildlife Officers, working with officials of the Wildlife Protection Society of India, searched a shop owned by the Renaissance Corporation in Mayfair, London. During the search 138 shahtoosh shawls, priced at a total of £353,000, were seized. This was one of the largest seizures of Shahtoosh shawls in the world.

In April 2000 the company was convicted of keeping an endangered

species for sale and were fined £1,500. The shawls were ordered to be forfeited. This was the first successful prosecution against the illegal trade in shahtoosh in the West. The demand for shahtoosh emanating from places like London provides the incentive for the poaching of the Chiru in China. We are working to reduce the demand for shahtoosh by publishing advice and information for traders and consumers, and this, together with the extensive media coverage which the issue has attracted appeared to have had an impact on the trade here. However, we will continue our work against the illegal trade in shahtoosh in London.

Since the launch of Operation Charm, Metropolitan Police Wildlife Officers have seized over 20,000 endangered species items being sold illegally in London. Most of these were TCM products and ingredients, although Operation Charm is looking at all aspects of the trade in endangered species, and other seizures have included illegal taxidermy and live animals for the exotic pet trade.

Operation Charm is not anti-Chinese in nature. We respect the Chinese culture and traditions, but Charm is a serious initiative against the illegal trade in endangered species. The operation is ongoing.

• If you have any information contact the Metropolitan Police Wildlife Liaison Officer on 020 7230 3641.

© *Metropolitan Police Service (MPS)*

ADDITIONAL RESOURCES

You might like to contact the following organisations for further information. Due to the increasing cost of postage, many organisations cannot respond to enquiries unless they receive a stamped, addressed envelope.

Animal Aid
The Old Chapel, Bradford Street
Tonbridge, TN9 1AW
Tel: 01732 364546
Fax: 01732 366533
E-mail: info@animalaid.org.uk
Web site: www.animalaid.org.uk
Animal Aid aims to expose and campaign peacefully against the abuse of animals in all its forms.

Care for the Wild International
1 Ashfolds, Horsham Road
Rusper, RH12 4QX
Tel: 01293 871596
Fax: 01293 871022
E-mail: info@careforthewild.org
Web site: www.careforthewild.org.uk
Care for the Wild International provides immediate aid to wildlife in distress anywhere in the world.

Convention on International Trade in Endangered Species (CITES)
International Environment House
15 Chemin des Anemones
CH-1219 Chatelaine-Geneva
Switzerland
Tel: 00 41 22 917 8139/40
Fax: 00 41 22 797 3417
E-mail: cites@unep.ch
Web site: www.cites.org
CITES is a treaty that regulates international trade in certain protected species.

Friends of the Earth (FOE)
26-28 Underwood Street
London N1 7JQ
Tel: 020 7490 1555
Fax: 020 7490 0881
E-mail: info@foe.co.uk
Web site: www.foe.co.uk
FOE publishes a comprehensive range of leaflets, books and in-depth briefings.

Greenpeace
Canonbury Villas
London, N1 2PN
Tel: 020 7865 8100
Fax: 020 7865 8200
E-mail: gn-info@uk.greenpeace.org
Web site: www.greenpeace.org.uk
Works to protect the environment through peaceful direct action.

International Fund for Animal Welfare Charitable Trust (IFAW)
87-90 Albert Embankment
London, SE1 7UD
Tel: 020 7587 6700
Fax: 020 7587 6720
E-mail: info@ifaw.org
Web site: www.ifaw.org
IFAW works to improve the welfare of wild animals throughout the world.

The Mammal Society
15 Cloisters House
8 Battersea Park Road
London, SW8 4BG
Tel: 020 7498 4358
Fax: 020 7622 8722
E-mail: enquiries@mammal.org
Web site: www.abdn.ac.uk
The Mammal Society works to protect British mammals and halt the decline of threatened species.

Orangutan Foundation
7 Kent Terrace
London, NW1 4RP
Tel: 020 7724 2912
Fax: 020 7706 2613
E-mail: info@orangutan.org.uk
Web site: www.orangutan.org.uk
Supports the study, understanding and conservation of orangutans in their principal and native habitat.

Royal Society for the Protection of Birds (RSPB)
The Lodge, Sandy
Bedfordshire, SG19 2DL
Tel: 01767 680551
Fax: 01767 692365
E-mail: education@rspb.org.uk
Web site: www.rspb.org.uk
The RSPB is the charity that takes action for wild birds and the environment.

Scottish Natural Heritage (SNH)
12 Hope Terrace
Edinburgh, EH9 2AS
Tel: 0131 447 4784
Fax: 0131 446 2277
Web site: www.snh.org.uk
Works with Scotland's people to care for Scotland's natural heritage.

TRAFFIC International
219c Huntingdon Road
Cambridge, CB3 0DL
Tel: 01223 277427
Fax: 01223 277237
E-mail: traffic@trafficint.org
Web site: www.traffic.org
TRAFFIC is the world's largest wildlife trade monitoring programme and a global expert on wildlife trade issues.

World Society for the Protection of Animals (WSPA)
89 Albert Embankment
London, SE1 7TP
Tel: 020 7793 0540
Fax: 020 7793 0208
E-mail: wspa@wspa.org.uk
Web site: www.wspa.org.uk
WSPA works in co-operation with more than 300 member organisations in 70 countries to promote animal welfare and conservation.

WWF-UK
Panda House, Weyside Park
Catteshall Lane
Godalming
Surrey, GU7 1XR
Tel: 01483 426444
Fax: 01483 426409
E-mail: wwf-uk@wwf-uk.org
Web site: www.wwf-uk.org
WWF is committed to saving threatened wildlife species and their habitats.

Young People's Trust for the Environment and Nature Conservation (YPTENC)
8 Leapale Road
Guildford
Surrey, GU1 4JX
Tel: 01483 539600
Fax: 01483 301992
E-mail: info@yptenc.org.uk
Web site: www.yptenc.org.uk
Works to educate young people in matters relating to the conservation of the world's wild places and natural resources.

INDEX

agriculture, effects on wildlife 32
apes, orangutans 6, 14, 15

badgers 34
barn owls 30
basking sharks 23
bats 3, 29, 30, 34
bears 4, 18
beavers, reintroduction in Scotland 37
biodiversity, and wildlife 2, 5, 15-16, 26-7
birds, endangered species in Britain 29, 35
black-footed ferrets 5
blue whales 4
bonobo chimpanzees 15
brown hares 30, 34
butterflies
    illegal trade in 38
    loss of species in Britain 6, 32-3

chimpanzees
    at risk of extinction 15
    and vivisection 5
Chinese traditional medicine (CTM)
    stopping illegal trade in 39-40
    use of endangered species in 18, 23-4
    use of substitutes in 24
    use of tiger bones in 9, 10, 11, 23-4
CITES (Convention on International Trade in
        Endangered Species) 1, 2, 13, 16, 17, 18, 19, 20, 21
    and turtles 24
    and whaling 23
    and wildlife trade in the UK 38, 39
cloning, pandas 7, 8
condors, Californian 4-5

deforestation, and elephant habitats 13
dinosaurs 3, 26
dodos 3, 5
dormice 30, 34

elephants, conservation of 2, 5-6, 12-13, 22-3
endangered animals 1-5
    in Britain 28-31
    saving 5, 6
    trade in 17-19, 21-2, 24, 39-40
evolution, and animals 2
extinction
    animals facing 5-7
    and biodiversity 26-7
    direct, indirect and natural 6
    extinct wildlife in Britain 28, 30, 32
    and human activity 27
    natural rate of 15, 25
    process of 3, 25

ferrets, black-footed 5
fish, over-fishing 16
fish eagle, white tailed 4

golden lion tamarins 4, 27
gorillas, conservation of 1, 4, 5, 15
grey squirrels 37

habitat destruction
    and endangered animals 1, 3, 8
        in Britain 28, 30, 31, 33
    and the loss of biodiversity 16
hares 30, 34
hawksbill turtles 8, 20, 21-2, 23
hooded seals 5
hunting
    elephants 13
    and endangered animals 1-2, 3, 5, 20
    and the loss of biodiversity 16

ibis, Northern bald 3-4
ivory trade 13, 20, 22

Komodo dragons 4

lady's slipper orchid 29
leopards, trade in 18-19

macaque, lion-tailed 4
mammals, endangered British 28-9, 30-1, 34
mammoth cloning 8
mandarin ducks 4, 35
marsh warblers 29

natterjack toads 29
nightjars 29
numbats 4

oceans
    chemical pollution, and endangered animals 2, 16
    over-fishing of 16
oil spills, animals killed as a result of 16
orangutans 6, 14, 15
otters 28-9, 30

pandas 1, 6, 7-8
parrots, trade in 19
penguins, jackass 4
pine martens 30
plants
    endangered species 19, 29
    global trade in wild plants 38, 39
    saving Britain's rarest plants 34
polecats 30, 34
pollution
    and endangered animals 1, 2, 31
        in Britain 34
    and the loss of biodiversity 16
population growth
    and elephants 13
    and endangered animals 2-3
    and extinct animals 7

red squirrels 30, 34

42

* * * * *

The Internet has been likened to shopping in a supermarket without aisles. The press of a button on a Web browser can bring up thousands of sites but working your way through them to find what you want can involve long and frustrating on-line searches.

And unfortunately many sites contain inaccurate, misleading or heavily biased information. Our researchers have therefore undertaken an extensive analysis to bring you a selection of quality Web site addresses.

Friends of the Earth (FOE)
www.foe.co.uk
Click on Wild places under threat! and enter your keyword. This will bring up FOE's latest news on the relevant issue.

Greenpeace
www.greenpeace.org.uk
Use the pull down menu for information on the Amazon and also whaling issues. Alternatively, hit the search button and enter your keyword.

Care for the Wild International
www.careforthewild.org.uk
Has animal fact sheets on Elephants, Tigers, Rhinos, Chimps, Badgers, Otters, Bears, Orang-utans and British endangered species. You can also register on-line for a Schools Information pack.

WWF-UK
www.wwf-uk.org
Has new campaign with Department of the Environment, Transport and the Regions called Souvenir Alert. See web page www.wwf-uk.org/campaigns/alert1.htm

Royal Society for the Protection of Birds (RSPB)
www.rspb.org.uk
An impressive site. Click on Conservation Issues for useful information on the following: Climate change, Wetlands, Farming and wildlife, Marine action, Forestry, Site protection, Greening the economy, Wild birds and the law, and Birds of prey.

Mammal Society
www.abdn.ac.uk/mammal
The Mammal Society's educational aim is to broaden people's understanding of British mammals. This is a very thorough web site which looks at the issue of British mammals including endangered species. Factsheets are available on-line.

Young People's Trust for the Environment and Nature Conservation (YPTENC)
www.yptenc.org.uk
Has a wide range of on-line factsheets. Click on either Animal Facts or Environmental Facts to view a list of the available factsheets.

ACKNOWLEDGEMENTS

The publisher is grateful for permission to reproduce the following material.

While every care has been taken to trace and acknowledge copyright, the publisher tenders its apology for any accidental infringement or where copyright has proved untraceable. The publisher would be pleased to come to a suitable arrangement in any such case with the rightful owner.

Chapter One: The Worldwide Situation

Endangered animals, © Animal Aid, *Endangered animals of the world*, © Young People's Trust for the Environment (YPTENC), *Animals facing extinction*, © Animal Aid, *Extinction*, © Young People's Trust for the Environment (YPTENC), *Pandas poised on the precipice*, © Guardian Newspapers Limited, 2000, *Hawksbill turtle faces extinction despite years of conservation efforts*, © Guardian Newspapers Limited, 2000, *Tigers on brink of extinction*, © The Independent, April 2000, *A future for tigers?*, © People & the Planet, *Elephant facts*, © Care for the Wild International (CFTWI), *The Orangutan Foundation*, © The Orangutan Foundation, *Great apes put chimps at risk of extinction*, © The Independent, May 2000, *Life under threat*, © Greenpeace, *Trade in endangered species*, © Young People's Trust for the Environment (YPTENC), *The battle to save the world's rare wildlife*, © The Independent, April 2000, *Convention on International Trade in Endangered Species of Wild Fauna and Flora*, © Convention on International Trade in Endangered Species of Wild Fauna and Flora (CITES), *IFAW campaigns to protect endangered species*, © IFAW, *Traders say profit can be motive for preservation*, © Guardian Newspapers Limited, 2000, *Threatened species in traditional medicines*, © TRAFFIC, *Medicinal wildlife trade*, © TRAFFIC, *The trouble with tourists*, © World Society for the Protection of Animals (WSPA), *Getting the measure of extinction*, © People & the Planet, *Extinct – so what?*, © Royal Society for the Protection of Birds (RSPB), *The impact of man*, © The Independent, March 2000.

Chapter Two: The Situation in the UK

British endangered species, © Care for the Wild International (CFTWI), *Endangered British mammals*, © The Mammal Society, *Threatened British wildlife and habitats*, © WWF-UK, *Our countryside at risk*, © Friends of the Earth (FOE), *A green and pleasant land?*, © The Mammal Society, *Charity's plea to save rare plants*, © Telegraph Group Limited, London 2000, *Lowest ebb on record for many UK birds*, © Royal Society for the Protection of Birds (RSPB), *Species action programme*, © Scottish Natural Heritage (SNH), *Beavers make a comeback in Scotland*, © Telegraph Group Limited, London 2000, *Wildlife trade in the UK*, © TRAFFIC, *Operation Charm*, © Metropolitan Police Service (MPS).

Photographs and illustrations:

Pages 1, 7, 11, 16, 21, 35: Pumpkin House, pages 9, 13, 17, 19, 26, 30, 36, 40: Simon Kneebone.

Craig Donnellan
Cambridge
September, 2000